# COLLINS

# OUTDOOR DIY PROJECTS

*in a weekend*

# COLLINS

# OUTDOOR DIY PROJECTS
## in a weekend

JACKSON · DAY

HarperCollins*Publishers*

## COLLINS
## OUTDOOR DIY PROJECTS
## IN A WEEKEND

CONCEIVED, EDITED
AND DESIGNED AT INKLINK,
GREENWICH, LONDON, ENGLAND

Text:
Albert Jackson and David Day

Design and art direction:
Simon Jennings

Text editor:
Peter Leek

Illustrators:
Robin Harris and David Day

Studio photography:
Ben Jennings

Additional photography:
*For a full list of photographers
and copyright owners see
acknowledgments page 128*

First published in 1998
by HarperCollins Publishers,
London

Copyright
© HarperCollins Publishers, 1998

All rights reserved. No part of this
publication may be reproduced,
stored in a retrieval system, or
transmitted in any form or by any
means, electronic, mechanical,
photocopying, recording or otherwise, without the prior written
permission of the copyright owners.

A CIP catalogue record is available
from the British Library

ISBN 0 00 414045 1

Text set in Copperplate and Sabon
by Inklink, London

Printed in Italy by Rotolito Lombarda, Milan

Jacket photographs: Ben Jennings

Some of the text
and illustrations in
*Collins Outdoor
DIY Projects in a Weekend*
were previously published in
*Collins Complete DIY Manual*

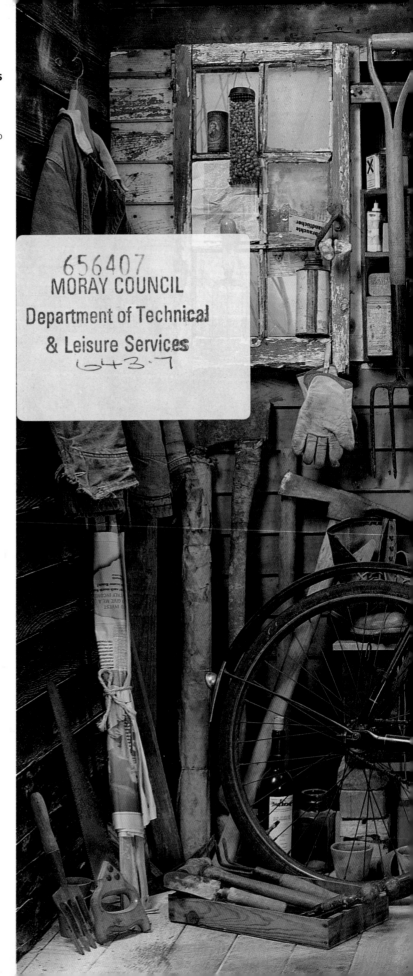

656407
MORAY COUNCIL
Department of Technical
& Leisure Services
643.7

# INTRODUCTION

Rain, sun and high winds combine to frustrate our efforts at keeping our homes and gardens looking spick-and-span, and every spring seems to herald a new round of essential maintenance. If that were not enough, we also have to find the time to make those improvements we've been promising ourselves all winter, and then make sure that everything is shipshape before the inclement weather returns. Time is short, so to help you make the most of your precious weekends, we have selected some of the more essential and popular outdoor DIY projects and suggested how much time you need to complete them. The simpler tasks should take no more than an hour or two, but other jobs are more time-consuming, and you will have to allow for a whole day's work or even an entire weekend. In some cases, you might have to spread the work over several weekends, in order to allow enough time for paint to dry or concrete to set. In any case, not everybody works at the same speed. If you are fairly experienced, you will probably cruise through some of these tasks in less time than we suggest; but if you are new to the game, it is bound to take you longer, in which case try to pace yourself so that you can leave a project at a stage where you can pick it up conveniently the following weekend. Remember to buy all the materials you need in advance, and check our list of essential tools for each project to make sure you have everything to hand for when you are ready to start work.

ALLOW A COUPLE OF HOURS

# 1

## A
## COUPLE
## OF HOURS

# CONTENTS

# 1

## A
## COUPLE
## OF HOURS

**ALLOW A COUPLE OF HOURS**

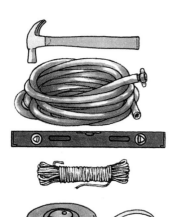

**Essential tools**

Hammer

Hosepipe

Long straightedge

Short wooden stakes

Spirit level

Strong twine

Tape measure

# TIPS FOR PLANNING YOUR GARDEN

Designing a garden is not an exact science. Plants and shrubs may not thrive even when you select species recommended for your particular soil conditions and for the amount of sunlight your garden receives; and trees may never reach the size specified in a catalogue. Nevertheless, forward planning produces a more satisfactory result than a haphazard approach, which may cause expensive mistakes – like laying a patio where it will be in shade for most of the day, or digging a fish pond that is too small to create the required conditions for the fish. It is these permanent features you should concentrate on planning first, at the same time keeping in mind how they will fit with planted and turfed areas of the garden.

**There's no rush**
Designing a complete garden can take a long time. When you move into a new home, it may well pay to delay major decisions about the garden for at least twelve months, so you can make notes on how the conditions change from season to season. This also gives you the opportunity to experiment with different garden arrangements and to sketch your ideas on paper – pleasant and useful ways to spend your time, if only for a couple of hours at a stretch.

# DECIDING ON THE APPROACH

Before you put pencil to paper, think about the type of garden you want and ask yourself whether it will sit happily with your house and its immediate surroundings. Is it to be a formal garden, laid out in straight lines or geometric patterns – a style that often marries successfully with modern architecture? Or do you prefer the more relaxed style of a rambling cottage garden? If you opt for the latter, remember that natural informality may not be as easy to achieve as you think, and your planting scheme will probably take several years to mature into the romantic garden that you have in mind. Or maybe you are attracted by the idea of a Japanese-style garden – a blend of both styles, with every plant, stone and pool of water carefully positioned, so that it bears all the hallmarks of a man-made landscape yet conveys a sense of natural harmony.

**A garden for all tastes**
*Good garden design does not rely on having a large plot of land. Here, curvilinear shapes draw the eye through a delightful array of foliage and flowers planted around a beautifully manicured lawn and a small but perfectly balanced fish pond.*

### Getting inspired

*There is no shortage of material from which to draw inspiration – there are countless books and magazines devoted to designing and planning gardens. Since no two gardens are completely alike, you probably won't find a plan that fits your plot exactly, but you may well be able to adapt a particular approach or develop a small detail into your own design.*

*Visiting other gardens is an even better way of getting ideas. Although large country estates and city parks are designed on a much grander scale, they at least enable you to see how mature shrubs look or how plants, stone and water have been used in a rockery or water garden. Don't forget that friends may also have had to tackle problems similar to yours – if nothing else, you may be able to learn from their mistakes!*

# MEASURING UP

In order to make the best use of your particular plot of land, you need to take fairly accurate measurements and check the prevailing conditions.

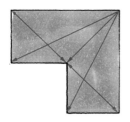

**Taking overall measurements**
*Note down the overall dimensions of your garden. At the same time, check the diagonal measurements, because a garden that appears to be exactly rectangular or square may not in fact be so. The diagonals are especially important when plotting irregular shapes.*

**Keep any useful features**
Plot the position of features you want to retain in your plan, such as existing pathways, areas of lawn, established trees, and so on.

**TIP** ● ● ● ● ● ● ● ● ● ● ● ● ●
**Soil conditions**
The type of soil you have in your garden will of course influence your choice of plants, although you can easily adjust soil content by adding peat or fertilizers. Clay soil, which is greyish in colour, is heavy when wet and tends to crack when dry. A sandy soil feels gritty and loose in dry conditions. Acidic peat soil is dark brown and flaky. Pale-coloured chalky soil, which often contains flints, will not support acid-loving plants. Any soil that contains too many small stones or gravel is unsuitable as topsoil.

**Making a note of slopes and gradients**
*Check how much the ground slopes. An accurate survey is not necessary, but at least jot down the direction of the slope and plot the points where it begins and ends. You can get some idea of the differences in level by using a long straightedge and a spirit level. Place one end of the straightedge on the top of a bank, for example, and measure the vertical distance from the other end to the foot of the slope.*

**Using a steep gradient to advantage**
*Some of the most dramatic gardens have resulted from having to contend with a sloping site. The photograph above shows how retaining walls can be used to terrace a steep bank of colourful shrubs.*

**How about the weather?**
Check the passage of the sun and the direction of prevailing winds. Don't forget that the angle of the sun will be higher in summer, and a screen of deciduous trees will be less effective as a windbreak when they drop their leaves.

Armed with all the measurements you have taken, make a simple drawing to try out your ideas. Then mark out the shapes and plot the positions of the important features in your garden, to make sure that your plan will work in reality.

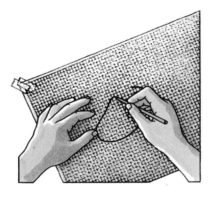

### Drawing a plan

*Draw a plan of your garden on paper. It must be a properly scaled plan or you are sure to make some gross errors, but it need not be professionally perfect. Use squared graph paper to plot the dimensions – but do the actual drawing on tracing paper laid over the graph paper, so you can try out several ideas and adapt your plan without having to redraw it every time.*

### TIP ● ● ● ● ● ● ● ● ● ● ● ● ●

### Common-sense safety

Don't make your garden an obstacle course. For example, a narrow path alongside a pond may be intimidating to an elderly relative, and low walls or planters near the edge of a patio could cause someone to trip.

### Plotting your design

Planning on paper is only the first stage. Gardens are rarely seen from above – it is therefore essential to plot the design on the ground, so you can check your dimensions and view the features from different angles.

A pond or patio that seems enormous on paper may look pathetically small in reality. Other shortcomings, such as the way a tree will block the view from your proposed patio, become obvious once you lay out the plan full size.

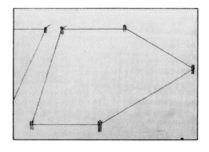

*1 Plot individual features by driving pegs into the ground and stretching string lines between them.*

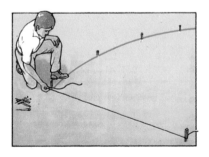

*2 Scribe arcs on the ground with a rope tied to a peg, and mark the curved lines with stakes or a row of bricks.*

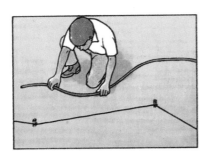

*3* Use a garden hose to mark out less regular curves and ponds. If you can scrape areas clear of weeds, that will define the shapes still further.

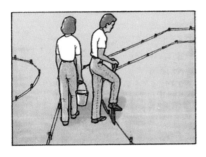

*4* When you have marked out your design, carry out a few experiments to check that it is practicable. Will it be possible, for instance, for two people to pass each other on a path without having to step into the flowerbeds?

**TIP** ● ● ● ● ● ● ● ● ● ● ●
**Siting a pond**
Site a pond away from overhanging trees and in an area where it will catch at least half the day's sunlight. Check that you can reach it with a hose, and that you can run electrical cables to power a pump or night-time lighting.

*5* Can you set down a wheelbarrow on the path without one of the legs slipping into a flowerbed?

*6* Try placing some furniture on the area you have marked out for a patio, to make sure there is enough room to relax comfortably or sit down to a meal with visitors.

*7* Allow a minimum width of 3m (9ft 9in) for a driveway, making sure there is enough room to open the doors of cars parked alongside a wall. If possible, allow room for the turning circle of your car. And make sure that when you pull out into the road you will have a clear view of the traffic.

*8* Bear in mind that vehicles larger than your own may need to use the drive or parking space.

**ALLOW A COUPLE OF HOURS**

**A CORDLESS DRILL IS
IDEAL FOR OUTDOOR WORK**

**Essential tools**

Electric drill and bits

Garden spade

Spanner

Spirit level

Trowel

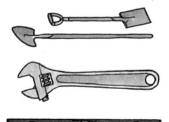

See also:
Replacing a fence post, page 34

# QUICK FIX FOR A ROTTING FENCE

Buried timber fence posts often rot below ground level, leaving a perfectly sound section above. Eventually a strong wind snaps the weakened wood – and before you know it the whole fence begins to sway, putting additional strain on the remaining posts.

   The best option is to replace the damaged fence post, but you can make a passable repair by bracing the upper section with a short concrete post known as a spur, which comes ready-made with holes for bolting it to the sound section of the fence post using coach screws (woodscrews with square heads).

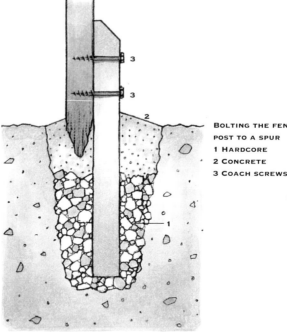

BOLTING THE FENCE
POST TO A SPUR
1 HARDCORE
2 CONCRETE
3 COACH SCREWS

**Erecting the spur**
*Dig the soil from around the rotted stump and remove it. Insert the concrete spur in the hole and pack hardcore around it. Make sure the spur is upright, then fill the hole with concrete.*

   *Drill pilot holes in the wooden post for the coach screws and, using a spanner, draw the post tightly against the spur. Smooth the concrete around the spur with a trowel.*

# STOPPING YOUR POND OVERFLOWING

Every garden pond needs topping up from time to time – and as many gardeners know to their cost, it is all too easy to forget to turn off the water and flood the garden when the pond overflows. As a precaution, build a simple drain beneath the pond's edging stones to allow excess water to escape. This also provides a means of running electric flex into the pond to power a pump or lighting.

**ALLOW A COUPLE OF HOURS**

**Essential tools**

Hacksaw or tenon saw

Pop riveter

*1 Cut corrugated-plastic sheet into two strips about 150mm (6in) wide and long enough to run under the edging stones. Pop-rivet the strips together to make a channel about 25mm (1in) deep.*

*2 Scrape earth and sand from beneath the pond liner in order to accommodate the channel, then lay edging stones on top to hold it in place.*

*Dig a small soakaway behind the channel and fill it with rubble topped with fine gravel or turf up to the level of the stones.*

**ALLOW A COUPLE OF HOURS**

**Essential tools**

Electric drill

Hammer

Masonry bit

Pliers

**Fixing a trellis to a wall**
*You can buy trellis panels
made from treated timber
or from polystyrene that
come in a range of sizes
and shapes. There are also
expanding trellises, which
you open out to a width
that is suitable for your
particular location.
Attach the trellis to the
masonry, using rust-proof
screws driven into wall
plugs. A plastic trellis
spacer or short strip of
wood slipped around each
screw will hold the trellis
away from the wall, to
provide a clear path for
the climbing plants.*

See also:
Brightening up a dull wall, page 118
Refurbishing an old wall, page 64

# CAMOUFLAGING AN UGLY WALL

Since brick and stone are attractive building
materials, they rarely require any form of
embellishment to make them acceptable.
Indeed, unless painting walls is the tradition in
your part of the country, masonry is generally
best left unfinished. But if you look out onto
the end of a terrace of houses or the back wall
of an extension, you may want to disguise the
expanse of featureless masonry with climbing
plants such as ivy, clematis or Virginia creeper.

# PROVIDING
# SUPPORT FOR CLIMBERS

Because the adventitious roots of ivy grip the surface of a wall, a mature plant does not need further support. Similarly, Virginia creeper has sticky tendrils that will adhere to the masonry. However, both plants require training wires or a supporting trellis to get them started and to help them climb in the required direction. Both clematis and passion flowers need wires or a trellis as anchor points for their clinging tendrils.

## PUTTING UP TRAINING WIRES

Run lengths of galvanized or plastic-covered training wire up or across the wall. Place the wires about 450mm (1ft 6in) apart.

*1* *At each end of each run of wire, drill and plug a hole for a long screw eye.*

*2* *Twist one end of the training wire through one of the screw eyes.*

*3* *At about 2m (6ft) intervals, thread the wire through a stamped-metal vine eye driven into the pointing. Twist the wire onto another screw eye at the far end.*

*4* *Attach the plant stem to the wire using plastic split rings or garden ties, or tie it loosely with garden twine.*

### Will ivy harm masonry?

There is a widely held belief that climbing plants, especially ivy, will damage any masonry wall. If exterior rendering or the mortar between bricks or stonework is in a poor condition, then a vigorous ivy plant will undoubtedly weaken the structure as its aerial roots attempt to extract moisture from the masonry. The roots will invade broken joints or rendering and, on finding a source of nourishment for the plant, will expand and burst the weakened material, thus encouraging damp to penetrate.

However, with sound bricks and mortar ivy can do no more than climb with the aid of training wires and its own suckerlike roots, which do not provide nourishment but are for support only.

So long as the structure is sound and free from damp, there is even some benefit in allowing a plant to clothe a wall, since its close-growing mat of leaves, mostly with their drip tips pointing downwards, acts as insulation and provides protection against the elements.

### TIP ● ● ● ● ● ● ● ● ● ● ● ● ●

**Keeping climbers under control**

Climbers must be pruned regularly, so that they do not penetrate between roof tiles or slates or clog drainpipes and gutters.

If a robust climber is allowed to grow unchecked, the weight of the mature plant may eventually topple a weakened wall.

**ALLOW A COUPLE OF HOURS**

**Essential tools**

Club hammer

Garden spade

Small trowel

# LEVELLING A LOOSE PAVING SLAB

Unless paving is firmly bedded on a layer of concrete, the long-term effects of rainwater, ants or tree roots can cause one or more slabs to become unstable. If you discover that a paving slab rocks every time you step on it, level the slab without delay – before it causes someone to trip.

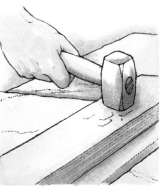

*2 Level the exposed area, adding hardcore or sharp sand to fill hollows and tamping it flush with a stout piece of wood.*

*4 Lower the slab into place and position it centrally, using the tip of the spade. Lay a stout wooden batten across the slab and tap it down with a club hammer until the slab is flush with the ones surrounding it.*

*1 Insert the tip of a spade into the joint on one side of the loose slab, and lever it carefully out of its recess.*

*3 Make a stiff mortar, using 1 part cement to 4 parts builder's sand. Put a fist-size blob of mortar in each corner of the recess, and one more in the middle.*

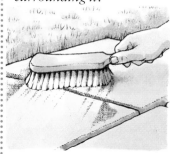

*5 Brush a dry mortar mix (1 part cement to 3 parts sand) into the joints and sprinkle it lightly with water. Don't step on the slab for at least 24 hours.*

# LOPPING BRANCHES

Most trees require no more than light pruning to keep them in shape and prevent them casting too much shadow over your garden. If you want to reduce the height of a large tree or remove a tree that appears to be damaging neighbouring property, always seek the advice of a professional tree surgeon and contact your local authority to check whether the tree is protected. Obtaining official permission to fell trees is especially relevant if you live in a conservation area. Consult your neighbours, and think carefully before you do anything to a mature tree that might harm it or spoil the local environment.

**ALLOW A COUPLE OF HOURS**

**Essential tools**

Pruning knife

Pruning saw or log saw

Old paintbrush

**Removing damaged or diseased branches**

You can safely remove small diseased branches or trim back the remains of broken tree limbs, so long as you take adequate precautions to ensure that severed wood can fall harmlessly to the ground. Don't climb trees in order to reach damaged branches unless you can construct a secure working platform or harness yourself safely to the tree trunk.

The technique shown here is designed to remove a branch without the wood tearing back to the main stem or tree trunk.

Unless urgent treatment is required, it is usually best to wait until late winter or early spring before removing branches. However, some fruit trees (such as damson, plum and cherry) should only be pruned in midsummer.

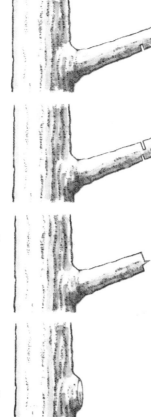

*1 Partially cut through the underside of the branch, about 300mm (1ft) from the main stem or trunk.*

*2 Make a second partial cut, this time through the upper side of the branch about 25mm (1in) further away from the trunk.*

*3 As the second cut comes near to the first, the branch will fall away, without stripping the bark of the tree back to the trunk.*

*4 Remove the remaining stump with a single saw cut, almost flush with the stem or trunk, then trim the rough edges with a pruning knife. Paint the cut end with a proprietary pruning sealant to protect the tree from disease, frost damage and excessive damp.*

**Essential tools**
Hacksaw

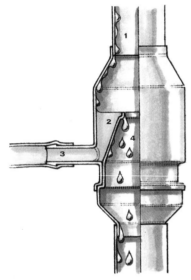

**Inside a diverter**
*Water running down the inside wall of the downpipe (1) is collected in a circular channel (2) and diverted into the filler tube (3) that runs to the butt. When the butt is filled to capacity, the channel overflows into the lower section of the downpipe (4).*

# SAVING RAINWATER

Long dry summers often create temporary water shortages that lead to a ban on using hosepipes for watering gardens. Conserving rainwater for your own use is good for the environment – and if you do not have an outside tap, it may be more convenient to fill watering cans from a water butt in the garden rather than use a tap in the house.

### Rainwater diverters and butts

By inserting a plastic diverter into a guttering down-pipe, you can deliver rainwater via a flexible filler tube into a storage butt standing alongside.

For a large garden, it is possible to couple two butts together, using another flexible tube. Alternatively, it may be convenient to fill one butt from a downpipe on the house and a second one from a garage or shed at the far end of the garden. Place each butt on a ready-made stand or build a plinth from concrete blocks, so you can place a watering can beneath the tap

There are a number of rainwater diverters on the market. Many of them will fit downpipes of various diameters; some can be adapted to take square pipes.

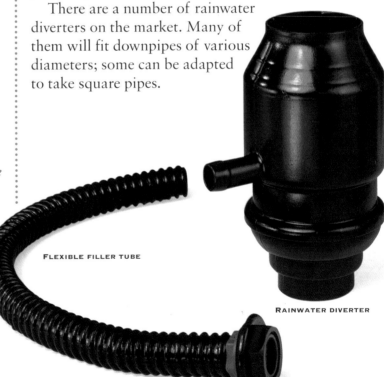

FLEXIBLE FILLER TUBE

RAINWATER DIVERTER

# FITTING A RAINWATER DIVERTER

Since each brand of diverter is slightly different, you will need to follow the manufacturer's detailed instructions.

The following describes the general principles for fitting a diverter into a circular downpipe.

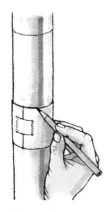

*1* Mark a line round the pipe, level with the top of the water butt, remembering to include the height of the stand or plinth.

Mark a similar line below the first. The exact location of this line will depend on the size of your diverter (see manufacturer's instructions).

*2* Cut out the section of pipe between the two lines, using a hacksaw.

*3* Locate the diverter on the end of the top section of downpipe, then slide it up the pipe until you can insert it into the lower section of the downpipe.

Swivel the diverter to direct its outlet towards the water butt.

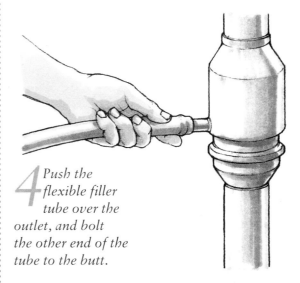

*4* Push the flexible filler tube over the outlet, and bolt the other end of the tube to the butt.

TO MAXIMIZE STORAGE, COUPLE TWO BUTTS TOGETHER

TIP ● ● ● ● ● ● ● ● ● ● ● ● ● ● ●
**Fitting a safe lid**
Make sure a water butt is sealed with a lid fitted with a child-proof catch. You may be able to buy a replacement if your water butt is not already fitted with this type of lid.

# PLANT PROTECTION

Newly planted shrubs and trees, especially conifers, are particularly vulnerable to the cold drying winds often prevalent from late autumn to early spring. The same seasons bring damaging frosts. As autumn approaches, take a few simple precautions to protect exposed plants.

## PROTECTING PLANTS FROM WIND

Permanent protection can be provided by planting hedges or screens of hardy trees and shrubs on the windward side of the garden (this is normally to the north or northeast). If permanent screening is impractical, there are a number of ways to provide temporary protection.

**Supporting bushy plants**
To help bushy plants withstand the punishing effects of wind, push twiggy sticks into the ground around them. Alternatively, insert garden canes and tie the plants to them loosely with twine.

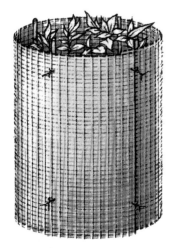

**Reducing the impact of icy winds**
*Effective protection can be achieved by screening plants with a material that will reduce the strength of the wind while allowing air to circulate. One way is to wire purpose-made reed or thatch screening to existing chain-link fencing or an open ranch-style fence. Alternatively, make a temporary cage from plastic windbreak netting or old sacking, wired or stapled to strong garden canes or wooden stakes.*

See also:
Providing support for climbers,
page 19

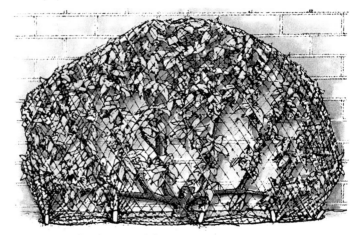

**Protecting climbers and fruit trees**
*Tie a blanket of windbreak netting over vulnerable climbers or fruit trees growing against a wall. Wire the netting to wall-mounted training wires or vine eyes and stake it to the ground.*

# FROST PROTECTORS

When planning your garden, give some thought to where frost is most likely to occur, and plant accordingly. Don't place susceptible plants in the lower parts of a site, because these are where cold air tends to collect.

As a matter of course, prudent gardeners lay a mulch of straw or peat around plants to prevent frost attacking at soil level. Hold straw in place with wire or canes.

**Protecting low-growing plants**
*Buy a plastic-tunnel cloche kit to protect a row of plants from frost. Each kit consists of a polyethylene cover that is stretched over polypropylene hoops driven into the soil. You can make a similar cloche from a sheet of plastic supported by a row of bent canes.*

**Screening taller plants**
*Cover small individual plants with clear-plastic bottles. Cut off the bottom of each bottle and press the cut edge into the soil. Stick short twigs into the soil around the plant to support the bottle cover from inside.*

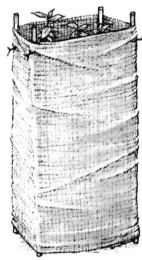

*Wrap sheets of plastic or sacking around canes to protect larger plants; or make a cane-and-wire tent stuffed with bracken, which will provide both wind and frost protection.*

**Staking freestanding trees**
*Young trees must be staked to provide them with support until they are strong enough to withstand strong winds. Dig a hole for the rootball of the tree and drive in a strong stake on the windward side of the hole.*

*Plant the tree and heel it in, then secure the stem to the stake just beneath the lower branches, using a tree tie – a plastic or rubber strap available from garden centres. Place the tie's buckle between the tree and the stake. If necessary, carefully saw the top off the stake so that it is the same height as the tree stem.*

# MAKING A GARDEN INCINERATOR

Vegetable matter and, to some extent, paper can be converted into compost for spreading on the garden. Some waste, however, will not break down readily and is best disposed of by burning in an efficient incinerator. Instead of buying a ready-made incinerator, you can make your own from an old metal dustbin or a pile of second-hand bricks. First, check that the burning of garden waste is not prohibited in your area.

**Essential tools**

Club hammer

Cold chisel

**Alternative tools**

Hole saw

Power drill

**Converting an old dustbin**

*An old galvanized dustbin can be turned into a useful incinerator – although it will eventually rust through, once the heat has removed the protective plating.*

*Half-fill the dustbin with sand and, using a cold chisel and club hammer, drive a series of randomly spaced holes all round the lower part of the bin. Wear protective leather gloves and goggles for this work.*

*Alternatively, for a neater appearance, drill round holes, using a 25mm (1in) diameter high-speed-steel hole saw fitted in an electric drill.*

*After emptying out the sand, make a few rainwater-drainage holes in the bottom, working from inside.*

*Stand the bin on old bricks or concrete blocks.*

YOU CAN FIT A METAL-CUTTING, HIGH-SPEED-STEEL HOLE SAW WITH A 25MM (1IN) DIAMETER INTO THE CHUCK OF AN ELECTRIC DRILL

See also:
Making a compost bin, page 50

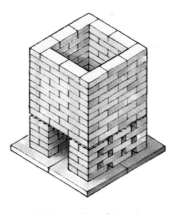

## Making a brick incinerator

*Choose a level site, away from the house and where there is no overhanging foliage. The incinerator is made from a total of 140 dry-laid bricks, to build a chamber 15 courses high.*

*Lay a square base, using four paving slabs, though this is not essential if the ground is well compacted.*

*For the bottom course, lay eight bricks to form a square, spacing the bricks 50mm (2in) apart. Make an ash hole by laying the middle brick end on, or use a half brick. Lay the next four courses in a similar manner, but work in alternate directions so the spaces are staggered. After building the first five courses, lay on a square of heavy-gauge wire mesh.*

*For the remaining 10 courses, use 10 bricks per course, butting their ends together and staggering the vertical joints.*

*When you are loading the incinerator, cut up branches into manageable sizes – don't ram in large pieces, as that can dislodge the bricks.*

BUILDING A BRICK INCINERATOR
1 PAVING-SLAB BASE
2 SPACES PROVIDE UPDRAUGHT
3 ASH HOLE
4 WIRE MESH
5 BRICK CHIMNEY

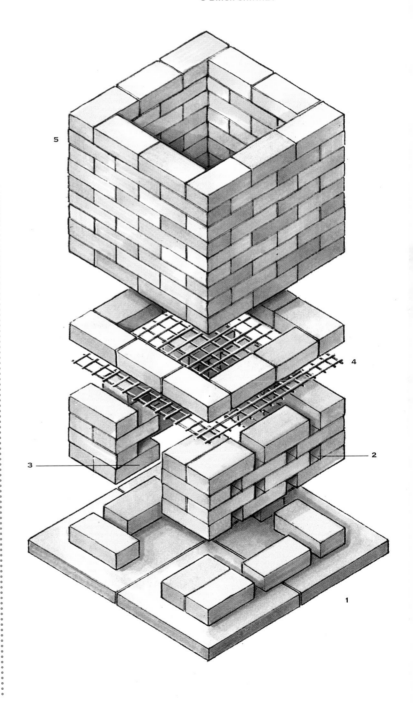

# 2

## A MORNING'S WORK

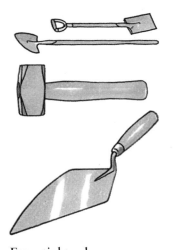

**Essential tools**

Spade or trowel

Club hammer

# LAYING STEPPING STONES ACROSS YOUR LAWN

It makes sense to pave regularly used routes (for example, from your back door to the garage or to a greenhouse at the bottom of the garden), especially if the toing and froing is wearing bald patches across the grass. If a continuous pathway would look too formal, lay a row of cast-concrete flagstones to serve as stepping stones – or, better still, use flat slabs of real stone.

*1 Cut around the edge of each stone with a spade or trowel, and remove the area of turf directly beneath.*

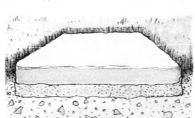

*2 Scoop out the earth to allow for a 25mm (1in) bed of sharp sand plus the stone, which needs to be about 18mm (¾in) below the level of the surrounding turf to avoid damaging the cutters of your lawn mower.*

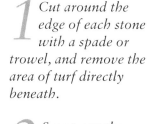

*3 Tap the stone into the sand until it no longer rocks when you step on it.*

**TIP** ● ● ● ● ● ● ● ● ● ● ● ● ● ● ● ● ●

**Merging with a patio**

You could combine a stepping-stone pathway with a patio laid with crazy paving. Create a broken edge to the patio, so the path merges naturally.

**MERGE STEPPING STONES WITH CRAZY PAVING**

# LAYING DECORATIVE COBBLESTONES

Cobbles, the large flint pebbles found on many beaches, can be laid loose, perhaps mingled with larger rocks and plants. Setting them in mortar or concrete creates a more permanent paved area. You can buy cobbles from large garden centres and some DIY stores.

**Bedding cobbles in concrete**
*Consolidate a layer of hard-core and cover it with a levelled layer of dry concrete mix about 50mm (2in) deep.*

*Press the cobbles into the dry mix, packing them tightly together and leaving them projecting above the surface.*

*Using a stout batten, tamp the cobblestones level, then lightly sprinkle the whole area with water, both to initiate the concrete-hardening process and to clean the surfaces of the cobbles.*

ALLOW A WHOLE MORNING

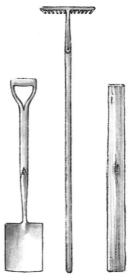

**Essential tools**

Heavy tamping batten

Rake

Spade

**Lay wet or dry**
*You can bed cobbles into concrete, leaving pockets here and there for plants (above). Or you can lay them loose to create a natural beach effect – attractive and labour-saving (left).*

See also:
Mixing concrete, page 111

31

ALLOW A WHOLE MORNING

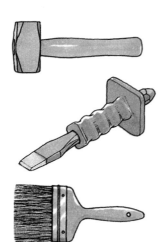

**Essential tools**

Club hammer

Cold chisel

Edging trowel

Metal trowel
or wooden float

Paintbrush

Safety goggles

See also:
Building a flight of strong steps,
page 94
Levelling a loose paving slab,
page 20
Repointing masonry, page 67

# MAINTAINING GARDEN STEPS

Inspect garden steps regularly to make sure they are not deteriorating beyond a safe condition. Replace cracked paving slabs, and secure any slabs that are loose or rocking. Repoint brickwork supports before the mortar starts to fall out, and replace rotting timber steps and risers.

**TIP**

**Don't let steps become slippery**

Algae tends to develop in damp conditions (especially under trees), and steps can become slippery if it is allowed to build up on the surfaces. Brush them with a solution of 1 part household bleach to 4 parts water. After 48 hours, wash with clean water and repeat if the fungal growth is heavy. Alternatively, use a proprietary fungicidal solution, following the manufacturer's instructions carefully.

As part of your routine maintenance, sweep wet leaves off steps and pathways.

# REPAIRING CONCRETE STEPS

Like other forms of masonry, concrete suffers from spalling: frost breaks down the surface and flakes off fragments of material. Spalling frequently occurs along the front edges of steps, where foot traffic adds to the problem. Repair broken edges without delay. Besides being ugly, with uneven edges the steps are not as safe as they might be.

*1 Wearing safety goggles, chip away concrete around the damaged area in order to provide a good grip for fresh concrete. Cut a board to the height of the riser and prop it against the step with bricks. Dilute some PVA bonding agent with water – say 3 parts water to 1 part bonding agent – and brush it onto the damaged area, taking care to stipple it into the crevices.*

*2 Mix a small batch of general-purpose concrete (1 part cement, 2 parts sharp sand and 3 parts aggregate), adding a little PVA bonding agent to help it stick to the step. When the surface becomes tacky, fill the hole with concrete mix, flush with the edge of the board.*

*3 Radius the front edge slightly with a home-made edging trowel, running it against the board.*

**Making an edging trowel**
*Bend a piece of sheet metal over a rod or tube that has a diameter of 18mm (¾ in), then screw a handle in the centre.*

*As you finish the surface of the concrete, run the radiused edge of the trowel against the board to keep the tool on a straight path.*

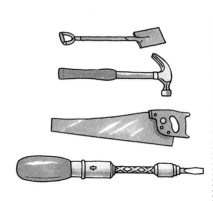

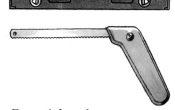

**Essential tools**

Garden spade

Hacksaw

Hammer

Panel saw

Screwdriver

Spirit level

*For post spikes*

Sledgehammer

Spanner

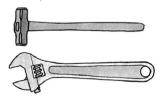

See also:
A quick fix for a rotting fence,
page 16

# REPLACING A FENCE POST

Strong winds play havoc with old fences, especially as it used to be the practice to bury the ends of the posts in nothing more than rammed hardcore. This, coupled with the fact the posts were not pressure-treated with preserver, as they are today, means that one or more posts can easily work loose or become seriously weakened by wet rot.

You can get away with quick fixes for a while, but eventually you are better off replacing suspect posts, if for no other reason than to preserve the appearance of a well-maintained fence.

It shouldn't take longer than half a day to replace a single post – although if you have set it in concrete, you will have to wait for the concrete to set before you can complete the job.

Choose a post that matches the size of the original, but remember to allow extra on the length – at least one quarter of the post should be buried to provide a firm foundation, and you need a bit extra so you can cut the post down to match the height of the fence after it is in place.

# PRESERVING FENCE POSTS

A new pressure-treated post will carry a substantial guarantee against rot – but if you can't get one that matches the colour of your fence, it pays to treat the new post yourself by soaking it in chemical preserver.

CLEAR      COLOURED      GREEN

### Types of preserver

There are clear solvent-based preservers that protect timber from wet rot only. Alternatively, use an all-purpose fluid that also provides protection against wood-boring insects. Most modern solvent-based products are harmless to plants when dry, but it makes sense to check this before you buy. Water-based preservers are odourless, and safe to use on horticultural timbers.

Tinted preservers have the advantage of colouring the post while protecting the wood against rot. Various brown shades are available, intended to simulate the most common hardwoods. Solvent-based preservers are made with light-fast pigments that inhibit fading. They do not penetrate as well as a clear preserver, but generally offer slightly better protection than the coloured water-based preservers.

# SOAKING THE POST IN PRESERVER

Any wood in contact with the ground benefits from prolonged immersion in preserver. You should at least stand the fence post on end in a bucket of fluid overnight.

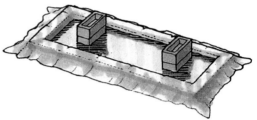

*1 For better protection, make a shallow bath from loose bricks and line it with thick polyethylene sheet. Fill the trough with preserver and immerse one or more of the posts, weighing them down with bricks to prevent them from floating.*

*2 Cover the trough and leave the wood to soak overnight. To empty the bath, sink a bucket at one end of the trough, then remove the bricks at that end so the fluid will pour out. Let the post dry out for 24 hours.*

### TIP ● ● ● ● ● ● ● ● ● ● ● ●

**Safety with preservers**

Solvent-based preservers are flammable – so do not smoke while using them, and extinguish any naked lights. Wear protective gloves and goggles when applying preservers. Wash spilt preserver from your skin and eyes with water immediately, and get medical advice if irritation persists.

# REMOVING THE OLD POST

Support the panel on each side of the fence, using long strips of wood wedged firmly under the top strip or the arris rail.

*1 Cut the old post free, using a hacksaw blade to sever nail fixings.*

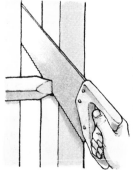

*2 If the post is attached to a closeboard fence, remove the first vertical board on each side of the post and then saw through the arris rails.*

*3 Removing the topsoil from around the post may loosen it sufficiently for you to pull it out. If the post is bedded firmly, or sunk into concrete, lever it out with a stout batten. First, drive large nails into two opposite faces of the post, about 300mm (1ft) from the ground. Then bind a length of rope around the post just below the nails and tie the ends to the tip of the batten. Build a pile of bricks close to the post and use it as a fulcrum to lever the post out of the ground.*

# ERECTING THE NEW POST

Dig out the hole. If you experience difficulty in digging the hole to the required depth or want to use a post-hole auger, remove one or both of the fence panels to give you more room to manoeuvre.

*1 Pack the bottom of the hole with hardcore (broken bricks or small stones) to a depth of about 150mm (6in).*

*2 Put the post in the hole, using the panels as a guide to its position. Ram some more hardcore around the post to keep it upright, then fill the hole with concrete.*

*3 Nail the panels to the post or attach the severed arris rails, using end brackets made for the purpose. Check that the post is upright, and support the fence while the concrete sets.*

*4 Next day, cut the post to length. Cut it square and nail on a post cap, or simply cut a bevel and paint the end with preserver.*

# USING METAL SPIKES

If you don't want to go to the trouble of anchoring a fence post in concrete, you can plug it into the square socket of a metal fence-post spike driven into firm ground. Use a 600mm (2ft) spike for fences up to 1.2m (4ft) high, and a 750mm (2ft 6in) spike for a 1.8m (6ft) fence.

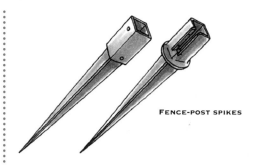

**FENCE-POST SPIKES**

*1 Place a scrap of hardwood post into the socket to protect the metal, then using the edge of the panel to position the spike, drive it partly into the ground with a sledgehammer.*

*2 Hold a spirit level against the socket to make certain the spike is upright, then hammer the spike into the ground until only the socket is visible.*

*3 Insert the new post and secure it by screwing through the side of the socket or by tightening clamping bolts, depending on the type of spike. Refix the panels and cut the post to length.*

**TIP** ● ● ● ● ● ● ● ● ● ● ● ● ● ● ●

**Fitting a spike into a broken stump**
If the old post has broken off flush with a concrete base, you can drive a special short spike into the end of the stump and then fit the new post in the usual way.

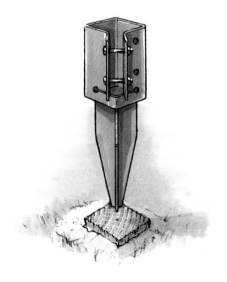

ALLOW A WHOLE MORNING

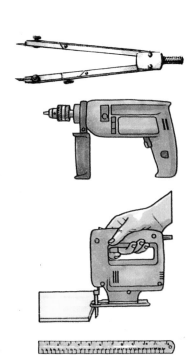

**Essential tools**

Pair of compasses

Power drill and bits

Power jigsaw

Ruler

# MAKING A HANGING BIRD TABLE

A well-stocked bird table will encourage birds to visit your garden, particularly in winter when food sources are scarce. Basically all you need is a simple platform hung from a tree or set on a post – but with only a little more effort you can make an attractive hanging table with feeding and drinking cups, and a woven fence that prevents food scraps being blown over the edge.

TIP ● ● ● ● ● ● ● ● ● ● ● ● ● ● ● ● ●
**A bird-feeder anchor**
As an additional food source, hang a proprietary wire-cage bird feeder from a screw hook driven into the underside of the table. A feeder hanging from the centre acts as an anchor that helps to keep the table on an even keel.

38

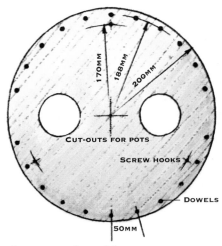

170MM  188MM  200MM

CUT-OUTS FOR POTS

SCREW HOOKS

DOWELS

50MM

## Marking out the table

Cut a 425mm (1ft 5in) square from 12mm (½in) exterior-grade plywood, and draw diagonals from each corner to find the centre of the square.

*1 Using a pair of compasses, mark out a circle with a radius of 200mm (8in), then mark a 188mm (7½in) circle inside the first.*

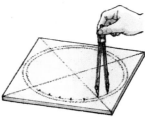

*2 Set the compasses to 50mm (2in) and, starting where one of the diagonals bisects the inner circle, mark off five equally spaced dowel centres on each side of the line for the fence posts.*

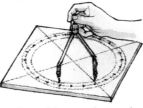

*3 To establish the positions for three brass screw hooks from which to suspend the table, mark another circle, with a radius of 170mm (6¾in), from the same centre. With the compasses set to the same radius, mark off six equally spaced points around the circle. Mark alternate points for positioning the three screw hooks.*

*4 Choose a pair of clean, shallow round plastic pots, such as used for food packaging, to use as feeder cups. Drill drainage holes in one of them. Mark out equally spaced holes in the table to receive the pots so they can be suspended from their rims.*

## CUTTING AND ASSEMBLING THE BIRD TABLE

Cut out the plywood disc with a power jigsaw, following the outer line. Sand the edge smooth. Also cut out the holes for the feeder cups.

On the marked centres, drill holes with a diameter of 6mm (¼in) to a depth of 9mm (⅜in) for the fence posts. Also drill pilot holes for the screw hooks. Sand the surface of the board ready for finishing.

For the fence posts, cut pieces of dowelling 38mm (1½in) long. Sand their ends, then glue them into place with a waterproof adhesive.

Finish the board with an acrylic exterior wood stain, and leave it to dry. Rub down and apply a second coat.

### Weaving the fence

*Weave straight hazel, willow or wisteria twigs between the posts to create a fence on each side. Add a dab of glue to the top twig where it touches each post.*

### Hanging the table

Insert the brass screw hooks into their pilot holes and hang the table from three lightweight chains cut to an appropriate length. Link the three ends of the chains with a shackle or S-hook. Suspend the table from a convenient support and drop the feeder cups into place.

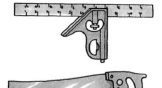

**Essential tools**

Hammer

Mitre square

Panel saw

Power drill and bits

Screwdriver

Try square

USING A NAIL SET

# A NESTING BOX FOR GARDEN BIRDS

A nesting box hung from a tree or screwed to a wall in a quiet corner of the garden will encourage small birds to set up residence.

You can make a box from an offcut of softwood floorboard, measuring 600 x 25mm (2ft x 1in). The size of the entrance hole will determine the species of bird that can use the box. Drill a 25mm (1in) hole for blue tits, or a 32mm (1¼in) hole for larger species of tit. For robins, which need a larger aperture still, make a shorter front panel, with a triangular opening above.

TREAT THE WOOD WITH AN ACRYLIC EXTERIOR WOOD STAIN. ALLOW IT TO DRY, THEN HANG THE BOX AT LEAST 2.5M (8FT) ABOVE THE GROUND.

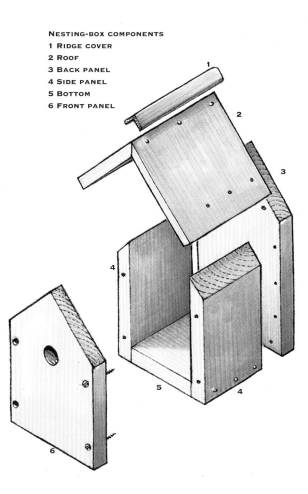

NESTING-BOX COMPONENTS
1 RIDGE COVER
2 ROOF
3 BACK PANEL
4 SIDE PANEL
5 BOTTOM
6 FRONT PANEL

## ASSEMBLING THE PARTS

Fix the mitred ends of the roof pieces together, using galvanized nails. Pin a length of wooden corner moulding along the ridge of the roof.

Nail the side panels to the ends of the bottom piece, with their ends flush. Nail the back panel to the sides and bottom.

Fix the front panel to the sides with countersunk brass screws. This will allow you to remove the front of the box at the end of the nesting season, so you can clean out contaminated nesting material.

Nail the roof in place through the back panel, then remove the front panel to fix the roof with nails from inside the box.

## Cutting the boards to size

*1 Start by cutting a 260mm (10¼ in) length off a floorboard. Then mark and saw it into two equal parts, cutting a 45-degree bevel through its thickness.*

*This single saw cut produces both halves of the pitched roof.*

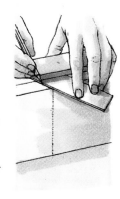

*2 Cut a piece of board 384mm (15in) long, and reduce its width to 100mm (4in).*

*For the bottom of the box, cut a piece 100mm (4in) long from one end of the reduced board.*

*3 To make the side panels, saw the remainder into two equal parts, cutting a 45-degree bevel across the board.*

*4 For the back panel, cut a 260mm (10¼ in) length of board. Mark and cut off the top corners at 45 degrees, to form a point at the centre. Drill a fixing hole 90mm (3½ in) below the apex.*

*5 Make the front panel, 200mm (7⅞ in) long, in a similar way. Drill an entrance hole through the panel about 80mm (3in) below the apex.*

ALLOW A WHOLE MORNING

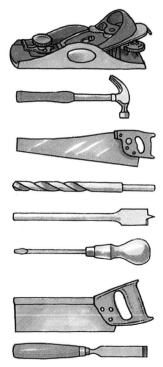

**Essential tools**

Block plane

Fast-action clamps

Hammer

Jigsaw or panel saw

Masonry bit

Nail set

Paintbrush

Power drill

Screwdriver

Spade bit

Tape measure

Tenon saw

Try square

Twist drills

Wood chisel

# WINDOW BOXES AND PLANTERS

A window box allows selected plants to be placed in full view of a window – providing an ideal way for people without gardens to cultivate and enjoy plants. In older houses with recessed windows, boxes can sit on the wide sills. But if the frames of your windows are more or less flush with the outside wall, then window boxes will need to be supported on metal brackets.

Planters are attractive containers for creating a display of garden plants on a patio or balcony. You can either make a planter to accommodate a large plastic tub or pot, or line the inside so the planter can contain soil.

# MAKING A WINDOW BOX

You can make a simple window box using 150 x 25mm (6 x 1in) softwood board, then paint or varnish it – but prior to finishing, it is essential to treat the wood with preserver.

Measure the width of the window opening for a box that is to sit on the sill; for one that will be hung from the wall on brackets, you need to measure the length of the sill itself. Cut three lengths of board slightly less than this dimension, and two end pieces to the appropriate size. Bore some drainage holes in the bottom panel.

### Decorating the front panel

You can leave the boards plain or decorate the front panel. To create the cloverleaf pattern shown here, set out a line of 25mm (1in) equilateral triangles spaced 150mm (6in) apart. Drill out the cloverleaf shape, using a 25mm (1in) spade bit centred on the points of each triangle. Use a chisel to trim off the points left by the drilling.

### Attaching the box with brackets

To mount the box on a wall, buy strong metal brackets to fit the depth of the box and fix them securely, using masonry wall plugs. Fix the box to the brackets with screws.

1 BACK PANEL
2 FRONT PANEL
3 BOTTOM PANEL
4 END PANEL
5 FILLET
6 SUPPORT

## ASSEMBLING THE BOX

*1 Glue and nail the bottom, back and front panels to the ends. Pin and glue triangular or quadrant fillets into the angle at the front and back.*

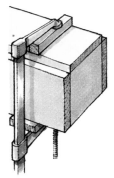

*2 Make three supports from 25 x 25mm (1 x 1in) softwood. Each support should be as long as the width of the bottom panel. Glue them to the underside of the box.*

*3 Plane the supports to accommodate the slope of the sill, so the bottom of the box is level. Fill the nail holes and finish the box with a polyurethane paint or varnish. Make a fitted liner from polyethylene sheet and pierce the material to make drainage holes. Place the box on the sill and fasten it to the window frame with wire ties.*

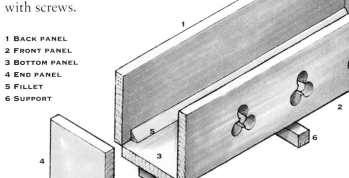

See also:
Types of preserver,
page 35

# MAKING A PLANTER

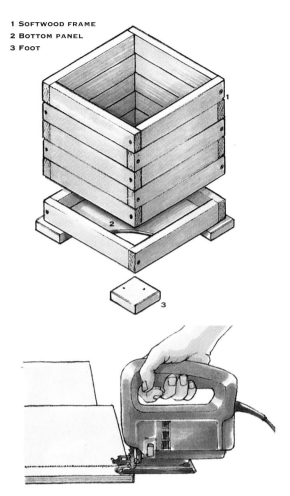

1 SOFTWOOD FRAME
2 BOTTOM PANEL
3 FOOT

Cut 24 equal lengths of 50 x 25mm (2 x 1in) softwood. Plane chamfers along all their edges. Drill a clearance hole for a screw in the side of each piece, 12mm (½in) from one end and level with the centre line. Soak the wood in preserver.

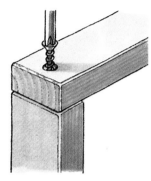

*1 Make six identical frames by gluing and screwing a butt joint at each corner. Check that the frames are square.*

*2 Glue the frames one on top of the other, alternating the direction of the corner joints to create a decorative effect with the end grain.*

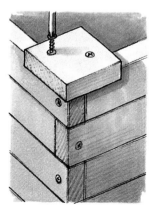

*3 Make four feet, each 75mm (3in) square, from wood 25mm (1in) thick, and chamfer their top edges. Glue and screw a foot under each of the corners, with only 12mm (½in) projecting on the two sides.*

*4 Cut a piece of exterior-grade plywood to fit inside the box and rest on the feet. Finish the planter with exterior wood stain or polyurethane varnish.*
*Line the box with plastic sheeting or fit a suitable pot.*

See also:
Types of preserver,
page 35

# STORING YOUR GARDEN TOOLS

Unless you are very disciplined, your shed or garage is likely to get cluttered with garden tools and other equipment. With careful planning and a few home-made gadgets, you can store your tools neatly so they are easy to find – and at the same time create space in which to move. It should take no longer than about half a day to complete any one project.

**ALLOW A WHOLE MORNING**

## LADDER STORAGE

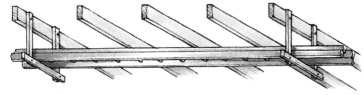

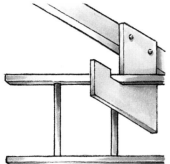

**RAFTER BRACKET**

### Long ladders
*Long extending ladders, used primarily for house maintenance, can be stored on suspended wooden frames bolted to the rafters of a garage. Alternatively, hang your ladders on wood or metal brackets fixed along a wall.*

### Hanging step ladders
*Step ladders, used for pruning or harvesting fruit, can be suspended vertically or horizontally on wood or metal brackets screwed to the garage wall.*

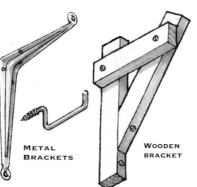

**METAL BRACKETS**

**WOODEN BRACKET**

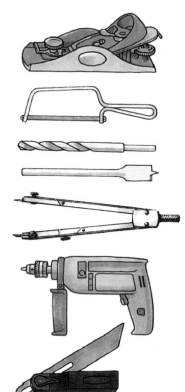

**Essential tools**

Block plane

Hacksaw

Masonry bits

Pair of compasses

Panel saw

Power drill and bits

Screwdriver

Sliding bevel

Spade bit

Tenon saw

Wood and metal files

Wood chisel

See also:
Laying a firm base for a tool shed, page 110

## MAKING A PEGGED HANGING RAIL

A simple line of 12mm (½in) dowel pegs fixed, at a slight angle, into a wooden rail provides convenient storage for a wide range of garden tools. Set in pairs, they will hold garden forks and spades, rakes and brooms. You can tie a loop of string through the handle of other tools and hang them from individual pegs. Use similar pegs to hang up your work clothes.

### Hooks and eyes
*Screw-in metal hooks and eyes provide a convenient means of hanging small handtools. Fit a screw eye in the end of each handle and hang them on a row of hooks screwed into a rail fixed to the shed or garage wall.*

### STORING A WHEELBARROW
*Tipping a wheelbarrow on end and fastening it to a wall saves space and prevents the barrow collecting rainwater. Screw a bevelled batten about 300mm (12in) from the ground to take the lip of the barrow. Screw a second batten, higher up, to fit between the handles when the barrow is resting on the lower batten. Fit wooden turn buttons to secure the handles.*

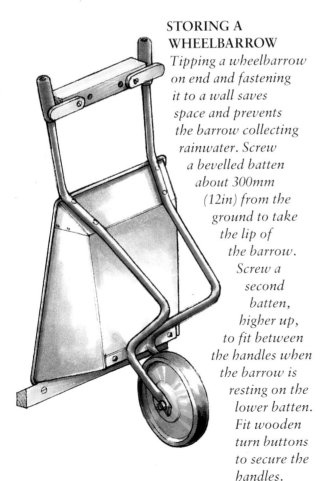

# STOWING A LAWN MOWER

Relatively small cylinder and hover mowers that have fold-flat handles can be usefully hung from a wall, but may be awkward to handle and heavy to lift.

To help make storage easier, make a pulley-operated pivoting frame that will lift and hold the mower against the wall. Make the width of the frame to fit inside the machine's handlebar.

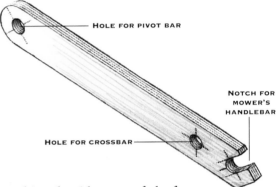

HOLE FOR PIVOT BAR

NOTCH FOR MOWER'S HANDLEBAR

HOLE FOR CROSSBAR

### Making the side arms of the frame
*Cut two 600 x 60mm (2ft x 2⅜in) side arms from plywood 18mm (¾in) thick. On each side arm, draw a diagonal line from both corners of one end, marking the centre for a 25mm (1in) diameter metal-tube pivot bar. Set a pair of compasses on this centre and mark a semicircle on the end. Mark the centre for a 25mm (1in) metal-tube crossbar, 120mm (5in) from the other end. Mark a 45-degree angled notch to suit the size of the mower's handlebar.*

*Drill the holes for the metal tubes, shape the end curves, then drill and saw out the notches at the ends.*

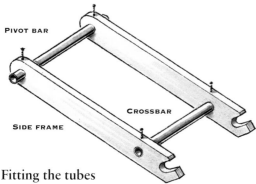

PIVOT BAR

CROSSBAR

SIDE FRAME

## Fitting the tubes

*Cut the crossbar tube to the required length; and cut the pivot-bar tube 50mm (2in) longer. Glue both tubes into the holes in the side arms with epoxy-resin adhesive. Set the crossbar flush with the outside faces of the arms, so that the pivot bar projects 25mm (1in) from each side. Drill pilot holes and reinforce the glued joints with self-tapping screws.*

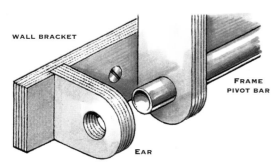

WALL BRACKET

FRAME PIVOT BAR

EAR

## Making the wall bracket

*Make a wall bracket from sections of 18mm (¾in) plywood 75mm (3in) wide to accommodate the pivoting frame. Mark, drill and shape the projecting 'ears' of the bracket as described for the pivoted ends of the side arms.*

*Cut 6mm (¼in) housing joints in the back rail for the ears. Assemble the bracket around the pivot bar of the frame, and screw and glue the ears into their housings.*

*Once the glue has set, screw the bracket to the wall at the required height to enable the mower to be lifted clear of the floor.*

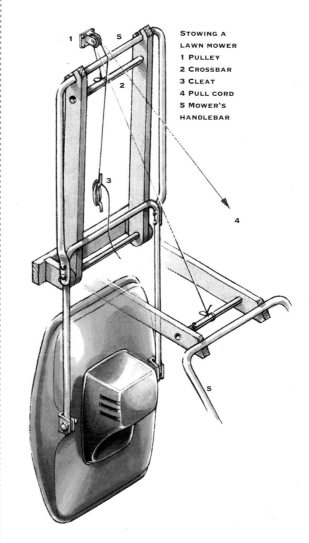

STOWING A LAWN MOWER
1 PULLEY
2 CROSSBAR
3 CLEAT
4 PULL CORD
5 MOWER'S HANDLEBAR

## Fixing the pulley

*Fix a pulley wheel to the wall above the frame's crossbar when it is in the raised position. Tie a length of cord to the crossbar and pass it through the pulley. Screw a cleat to the wall below the pulley for securing the pull cord.*

## Using the lifting frame

Release the pull cord and let the frame tip forward. Locate the handlebar of the folded mower into the notches and, using the cord, pull the frame into the vertical position. Tie off the cord to stow the mower securely.

# 3

## A
## WHOLE
## DAY

ALLOW ONE WHOLE DAY

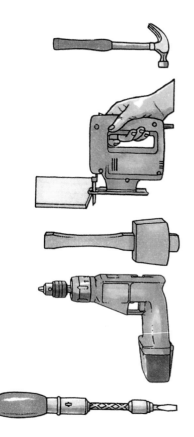

**Essential tools**

Hammer

Jigsaw

Mallet

Panel saw

Power drill and bits

Screwdriver

Tenon saw

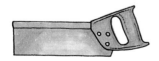

See also:
Types of preserver, page 35

# MAKING A COMPOST BIN

A wide range of ready-mixed composts is available for the cultivation of plants, either for potting seeds or cuttings, or use in plant containers, or to enrich your garden soil.

Both farm manure and well-rotted home-made organic-matter compost make ideal soil improvers. As well as being good for the garden, the latter provides a useful way to recycle kitchen and garden waste.

You can make garden compost from soft vegetative materials, including leaves, grass clippings, flowers and kitchen waste such as vegetable peelings. It should not contain woody branch material or roots, nor tough vegetable stems, such as cabbage, unless they have been shredded. Badly diseased or insect-ridden material and perennial weeds should always be rejected.

**Starting a compost heap**
*Begin with vegetable matter from the kitchen or garden.*

# DESIGNING A COMPOST BIN

A good compost bin needs to contain waste in a tidy manner, have an easy-to-load top and some means of extracting well-rotted matter at the bottom, and enclose the waste effectively enough to help generate heat and therefore speed up the rotting process. Ideally, two bins are better than one – so you are able to replenish one bin while continuing to extract rotted material from the other. There is a range of ready-made units on the market, but you can make your own from second-hand floorboards and wooden battens. A bin in the form of a 1m (3ft 3in) cube makes a useful single container. Double this for a twin unit.

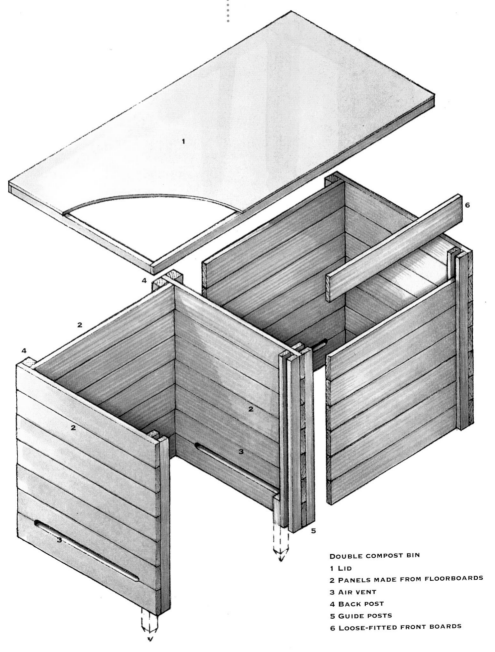

DOUBLE COMPOST BIN
1 LID
2 PANELS MADE FROM FLOORBOARDS
3 AIR VENT
4 BACK POST
5 GUIDE POSTS
6 LOOSE-FITTED FRONT BOARDS

# MAKING A SINGLE CONTAINER

Make the front, back and sides from second-hand 150 x 25mm (6 x 1in) floorboards. Saw them into 1m (3ft 3in) lengths. Cut sufficient boards to make up panels about 1m (3ft 3in) high when placed edge to edge.

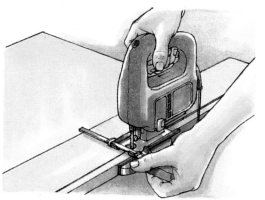

*1* Take the two bottom boards on each side and at the back, and cut away 12mm (½in) on their meeting edges, stopping about 150mm (6in) from each end. This will create air vents 25mm (1in) wide at the bottom.

*2* Cut two back posts from 50 x 50mm (2 x 2in) softwood to match the height of the side panels. Then cut four front guide posts from 50 x 25mm (2 x 1in) softwood to the same length. Treat all the parts with a wood preserver.

## ASSEMBLING THE PARTS
Make up the sides first.

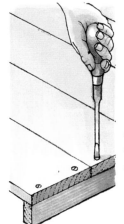

*1* With their edges butted together, screw the boards to a back post and to one of the front guide posts. Set their ends flush with the outside faces of the posts.

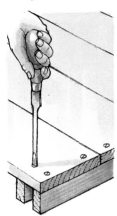

*2* Screw a second front guide post parallel to the first, leaving a space between them which is slightly wider than the thickness of the front boards. This forms a track to retain the loose-fitted front boards. Assemble the opposite side in the same way.

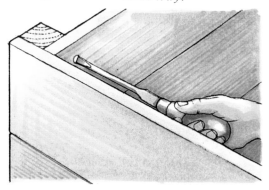

*3* Screw the back boards to the inside of the back posts. Set the assembly square and level on flat ground. Drive 50 x 50mm (2 x 2in) pretreated wooden stakes into the ground just inside the front posts. Screw the bottom side boards to the stakes. Drop the front boards into place between the guide posts.

## Making an extension unit

To make a twin compost bin, simply extend the first unit. Cut sufficient boards to make up another side panel and another back. Fix a back post and a pair of guide posts to the side of the first bin, then attach the back boards and additional side panel as described above.

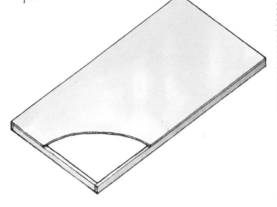

## Making the lid

Make a lid to fit over the top of the bin, to prevent rainwater from washing out nutrients and slowing down the rotting process by reducing the heat.

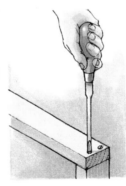

*1 Using 50 x 25 (2 x 1in) softwood, make up a simple butt-jointed glued-and-screwed frame to fit over the top of the bin.*

*2 Cut a sheet of thin exterior-grade plywood to fit the frame. Pin and glue it all round. Cover the lid with roofing felt, or waterproof it with paint or preserver. Also, to help retain heat, cover the compost heap with a piece of old carpet.*

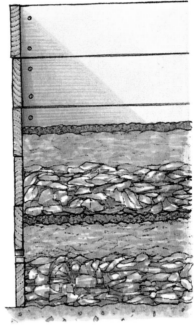

MANURE OR ACTIVATOR

WASTE VEGETABLE MATTER

MANURE OR ACTIVATOR

WASTE VEGETABLE MATTER

## TIP

### Making compost

Begin by building up a layer of mixed vegetable matter about 150mm (6in) deep. Sprinkle it with water.

Add a layer of farm manure or compost activator, available from garden centres. The latter is produced in granular form and as a liquid. Follow the manufacturer's instructions for quantities.

A thin layer of soil, about 12mm (½in) thick, is often recommended for the next layer, to introduce microbes and nutrients and to retain heat. However, if an activator is used, soil is not always essential.

Add another layer of vegetable matter, and repeat the layering process until the bin is filled.

After about 4 to 6 weeks, turn the heap over with a fork. Then leave to rot down for about 3 months.

**ALLOW ONE WHOLE DAY**

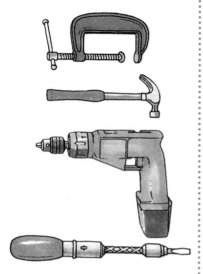

**Essential tools**

G-cramps

Hammer

Power drill and bits

Screwdriver

Spade

Spirit level

Trowel

# HANGING A GARDEN GATE

Although a well-made gate will last for years, eventually the ravages of wet rot and rust take their toll. When faced with replacing a gate, it pays to look for an exact replica, as you know it will fit between the posts and you can probably reuse the existing fittings. However, since manufacturers update their catalogues from time to time, trying to track down an identical gate may prove to be a fruitless task.

With luck, you may find a different style of gate that is an exact fit. Or a replacement only slightly wider than the original, so you can skim a little wood off the stiles until it fits well. A narrower gate may be accommodated by screwing a batten to each post, though that probably won't be a very elegant solution. Yet another option is to have a new gate made to measure – but that is likely to be relatively expensive, so you may be better off erecting a new pair of posts for a ready-made gate.

You can hang any gate in a day, but allow the complete weekend if you also have to set posts in concrete.

ABOVE:
DOUBLE GATES FOR
A DRIVE OR GARAGE
CENTRE:
WROUGHT-IRON SIDE
GATE TO A GARDEN
RIGHT:
SMALL-SCALE WOODEN
ENTRANCE GATE

# CHOOSING A NEW GATE

There are several points to consider when choosing a gate, not the least the cost. All gates are relatively expensive – but don't be tempted to buy one solely because it is cheaper than another. A gate must be sturdy if it is to be durable, and it must also be mounted on strong posts.

### Entrance gates
*An entrance gate tends to be designed as much for its appearance as its function. But it will be in constant use, so it pays to buy one that is properly braced, for example with a diagonal strut running from the top of the latch stile down to the bottom of the hanging or hinge stile. If you hang a gate with the diagonal strut running the other way, the bracing will have no effect whatsoever.*

*The most common fence structures are reflected in the style of entrance gates. Picket, closeboard and ranch-style gates are all available, as well as simple and attractive frame-and-panel gates. With the latter style of gate, the solid timber or exterior-grade plywood panels keep the frame rigid. If the tops of the stiles are cut at an angle or rounded over, they shed rainwater, reducing the likelihood of wet rot – a small but important point to bear in mind when you are buying a wooden gate.*

*Decorative iron gates are a frequent choice for entrances. When buying one, make sure the style is not too grandiose for the building or its location.*

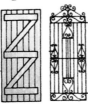

### Side gates
*A side gate is designed to protect a pathway next to a house from intruders. Side gates are invariably 2m (6ft 6in) high, and are made from wrought iron or stout sections of timber. Wooden gates are heavy and are therefore braced with strong diagonal members to keep them rigid. With security in mind, choose a closeboard or tongue-and-groove gate, since vertical boards are difficult to climb – and when you hang the gate, fit strong security bolts top and bottom.*

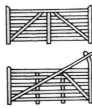

### Drive gates
*First, decide whether hanging a gate across a driveway to a garage is a good idea. For example, where will you park your car in order to open the gate? This can be a difficult and sometimes dangerous manoeuvre unless you have enough room to pull the car off the road with the gate closed.*

*Drive gates invariably open into the property, so check whether there is sufficient ground clearance for a wide gate if your drive slopes up from the entrance. An alternative is to hang two smaller gates that meet in the centre. If you decide on a wide gate, consider a traditional five-bar gate both for strength and for appearance.*

---

### Materials for gates
Many wooden gates are made from relatively cheap softwood – but a more durable wood, such as cedar or oak, is a better investment.

Most so-called wrought-iron gates are made from mild-steel bar, which must be primed and painted if it is to last any time at all.

# HANGING A GATE

The way a gate is hung on its post will vary, depending on the style of gate and type of fittings you choose to hang it from, but the principles are generally basically the same.

The method described here is for hanging a wooden entrance gate with strap hinges and an automatic latch.

1 Stand the gate between the posts, and prop it up on a pair of bricks or wooden blocks to hold it the required height off the ground. Tap in pairs of wedges on each side of the gate until it is held securely with sufficient gaps between it and the posts to accommodate the hinges and catch. When fitting strap hinges, the back faces of the gate and the posts should be flush.

See also:
Replacing a fence post, page 34
Erecting new posts, page 58

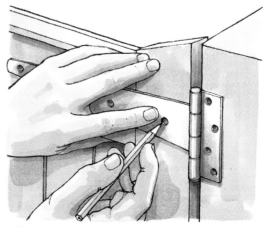

2 Use a spirit level to check that the top rail is horizontal, then hold each hinge in place and mark the screw holes. Drill pilot holes and drive in two screws for each flap on both hinges. Before inserting the rest of the screws, check that the gate can swing properly.

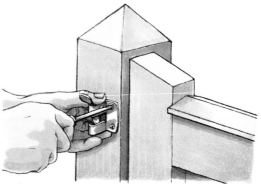

3 Fit the two parts of the catch in a similar way. Check that it operates easily before securing the fitting with all the screws.

**TIP** ● ● ● ● ● ● ● ● ● ● ● ● ●
**Fitting double gates**
When hanging a pair of gates between posts, clamp the two latch stiles together, with a suitable spacer sandwiched between them. Wedge the clamped gates between the posts and fit the hinges as described above.

# Hardware for Gates

You need specialized hinges and catches to take
the considerable strain that garden gates impose.

### Strap hinges
*Side gates and most wooden entrance gates are
hung on strap hinges or T-hinges. Screw the
long horizontal flaps to the gate rails; and the
vertical flaps to the face of the post. Heavier
gates need a stronger version bolted through
the top rail.*

*Wide drive gates need a double strap hinge
with a long flap bolted on each side of the top
rail. These heavy-duty hinges are supported by
bolts that pass through the gatepost.*

### Hinge pins
*On metal gates, metal collars welded to the
hinge side drop over hinge pins attached to
gateposts in a variety of ways. They may be
screw-fixed to timber posts; bolted through
concrete; built into the mortar joints of
masonry piers; or welded to metal posts.
Unless you either reverse the top pin or drill
a hole and fit a split pin and washer, the gate
can be lifted off its hinges at any time.*

### Automatic latches
*Simple wooden gates are fitted with a latch
that operates automatically as the gate is
closed. Screw the latch bar to the latch stile
of the gate and use it to position the latch on
the post.*

### Thumb latches
*Cut a slot through a closeboard side gate for
the latch lifter of a thumb latch. Pass the sneck
(lifter bar) through the slot and screw the
handle to the front of the gate. Screw the latch
beam to the inner face so that the sneck
releases the beam from the hooked keeper.*

### Ring latches
*A ring latch works in much the same way as
a thumb latch, but is operated by twisting the
ring handle to lift the latch beam.*

### Chelsea catches
*Bolt a Chelsea catch through a drive gate. The
latch pivots on the bolt to drop into a slot in
the catch plate screwed to the post.*

### Loop-over catches
*When a pair of gates are used for a drive
entrance, one gate is fixed with a drop bolt
located in a socket concreted into the ground.
A simple U-shaped metal bar, bolted through
the latch stile of the other gate, drops over the
stile of the fixed gate.*

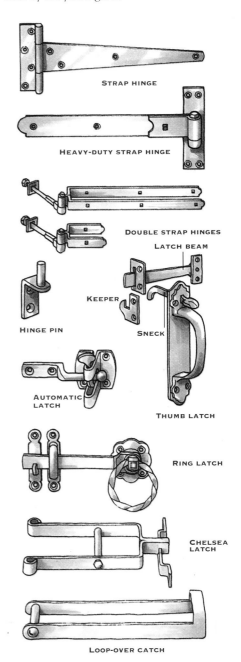

STRAP HINGE

HEAVY-DUTY STRAP HINGE

DOUBLE STRAP HINGES

LATCH BEAM

KEEPER

HINGE PIN

SNECK

AUTOMATIC LATCH

THUMB LATCH

RING LATCH

CHELSEA LATCH

LOOP-OVER CATCH

# ERECTING NEW POSTS

Gateposts and masonry piers have to take a great deal of strain, so they must be both strong and anchored securely in the ground. Use hardwood for wooden posts whenever possible, and select the section according to the weight of the gate. Posts 100mm (4in) square are adequate for most entrance gates, but use 125mm (5in) posts for gates 2m (6ft 6in) high. For a gate across a drive, choose posts 150mm (6in) or even 200mm (8in) square.

Concrete posts are a possibility – but unless you find a post predrilled to accept hinges and catch, you will have to screw them to a strip of timber bolted securely to the post.

Square or cylindrical tubular-steel metal posts are available with hinge pins, gatestop and catch welded in place. Like metal gates, they need to be painted to protect them from rust, unless they have been coated with plastic at the factory.

### Brick piers

*A pair of masonry piers is another possibility. Each of the piers should be a minimum of 328mm (1ft 1½ in) square and built on a firm concrete footing. For large, heavy gates, the hinge pier at least should be reinforced with a strong metal rod, buried in the footing and running centrally through the pier.*

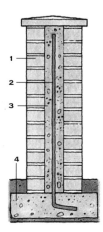

**REINFORCED BRICK PIER**
**1 BRICK PIER**
**2 METAL ROD**
**3 CONCRETE INFILL**
**4 FOOTING**

## ERECTING WOODEN GATEPOSTS

Gateposts are set in concrete like ordinary fence posts, but the post holes are linked by a concrete bridge to provide extra support.

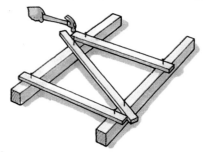

*1 Lay the gate on the ground, with a post on each side. Check that the posts are parallel and the required distance apart to accommodate hinges and catch. Nail two horizontal battens from post to post, and another diagonally to keep the posts in line while you erect them.*

*2 Dig a trench 300mm (1ft) wide across the entrance. Make it long enough to accept both posts. It need not be deeper than 300mm (1ft) in the centre, but dig an adequate post hole at each end: 450mm (1ft 6in) deep for a low entrance gate, and 600mm (2ft) deep for a taller side gate.*

*Set the battened gateposts in the post holes with hardcore and concrete, using temporary battens to hold them upright until the concrete sets.*

*At the same time, fill the trench with concrete and either level it flush with the pathway or allow for the thickness of paving slabs or blocks.*

*Having hung the new gate, fill nail holes with coloured putty.*

# CREATING A WATER FEATURE FOR YOUR PATIO

ALLOW ONE WHOLE DAY

One of the pleasures of a secluded garden is to be able to appreciate the natural sounds of rustling trees, bird song and, if you are particularly fortunate, the rippling tones of running water. As a rule, nature will provide the wind and the birds, but most of us have to supply the sound of running water ourselves.

Given sufficient space, most people opt for a fountain or a small cascade trickling into a garden pond. But what if you only have a small garden or patio? A space-saving water feature is the ideal solution. This need not involve more than a submersible recirculating pump placed in a miniature moulded-plastic pool set in the ground and covered with decorative pebbles. This type of water feature can be situated close to the house – within earshot of the windows and also conveniently placed for wiring into your power supply.

### Essential tools

Craft knife

Garden fork

Garden spade

Power drill and bits

Spirit level

Trowel

### Types of pump

Submersible pumps are made to provide a fountain, cascade or combination of both, and are produced in a range of sizes and performance. The manufacturers specify the performance of a pump in litres or gallons per hour, related to the height of the fountain spray or cascade volume. Pumps are powered by an electric motor, which is operated either by mains electricity or a low-voltage mains-powered transformer or, in some cases, by a solar-powered panel. They are fully insulated and supplied as ready-wired kits for connecting to your power supply. All the necessary fittings are generally provided, including a length of flexible hose.

For a patio water feature, choose a small cascade-type pump. If you are in doubt about the performance of a particular unit, check the manufacturer's literature or consult your supplier.

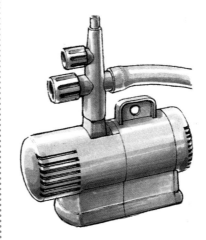

SUBMERSIBLE PUMP FOR A PATIO WATER FEATURE

# INSTALLING A MOULDED POOL

Moulded-plastic pools take the form of shallow round or square trays with a deep bucket-like centre section or sump. A perforated or moulded lid is provided to cover the sump, and to support the layer of pebbles used to disguise the feature once it has been installed.

### Excavating the pond

Start by digging a hole slightly larger than the size of the tray. Make the hole deep enough to set the edge of the tray level with or just below the surface of the patio. You also need to allow for a layer of sand – to be placed on the compacted base of the excavated hole – on which to bed the sump. Set the sump in place and partially fill it with water to help keep it steady. Carefully back-fill the sides with earth or sand; build up the infill until the sump and tray are well supported and level.

### Fitting the pump

Following the manufacturer's instructions, connect the pump's cable to your power supply, which must include a residual-current device (RCD) to protect the circuit.

Drill a discreet hole in a convenient door or window frame for the pump's cable, and seal the gap around the cable with silicone sealant. If you are in any doubt about the installation, consult an electrician.

Connect a length of hose to the pump's water outlet and place the pump in the sump, which you can now fill with water. Test the pump is working.

Lead the hose to one side and fit the lid in place. It may be necessary to trim the edge of the lid to accommodate the hose.

### Making the cascade

Two ceramic plant pots make an attractive cascade. Balance one of the pots at an angle on the rim of the other, and stand them on the tray. Feed the end of the hose into the drain hole in the bottom of the angled pot, then seal the hole with silicone sealant. This may be easier to do if you disconnect the hose from the pump once the hose has been cut to length.

With the pots in position, place some random-size decorative pebbles around them to cover the pond tray. Put a few pebbles inside the angled pot to weigh it down and to conceal the end of the hose.

Arrange potted plants to help disguise the hose at the rear. Run the pump, and place pebbles in and around the pots so as to create an attractive cascade.

### Routine maintenance

Top up the buried pond occasionally to make up for natural evaporation. At the end of the season, remove the pump and clean the filter. This will mean rearranging the pebbles, which provides an opportunity to remove leaf litter and clean up generally.

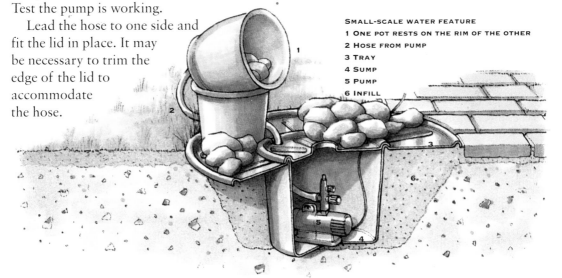

SMALL-SCALE WATER FEATURE
1 ONE POT RESTS ON THE RIM OF THE OTHER
2 HOSE FROM PUMP
3 TRAY
4 SUMP
5 PUMP
6 INFILL

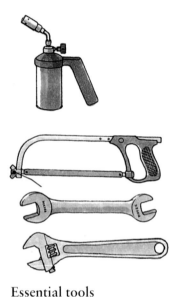

**Essential tools**

Blowtorch

Hacksaw/pipe cutter

Masonry bits

Power drill

Spanners

# LAYING ON A WATER SUPPLY

A bib tap situated on an outside wall is handy for attaching a hose for a lawn sprinkler, topping up a pond or washing the car.

To comply with bylaws, a double-seal non-return check valve must be incorporated in the plumbing to prevent contaminated water being drawn back into the system.

Also, it is advisable to incorporate a means of shutting off the water supply and draining the pipework during winter.

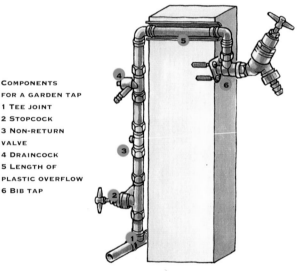

COMPONENTS
FOR A GARDEN TAP
1 TEE JOINT
2 STOPCOCK
3 NON-RETURN
VALVE
4 DRAINCOCK
5 LENGTH OF
PLASTIC OVERFLOW
6 BIB TAP

**Pipes and fittings to supply a garden tap**
*Turn off the main stopcock and drain the rising main. Fit a tee joint (1) in the rising main to run the supply to the tap. Run a short length of pipe to a convenient position for another stopcock (2) and the non-return valve (3), making sure the arrows marked on both fittings point in the direction of flow. Fit a draincock (4) after this point. Run a pipe through the wall inside a length of plastic overflow (5), so that any leaks will be detected quickly and will not soak the masonry. Wrap PTFE tape around the bib-tap thread before screwing it into a wallplate attached to the masonry outside (6).*

# PROTECTING YOUR FISH FROM CATS

Cats are attracted to fish swimming near the surface of a garden pond, although they often seem merely to be mesmerized by the movements of the fish rather than actively intent on poaching. However, a predatory cat can harm fish basking near the surface, even if it can't manage to scoop them out of the water.

The floating leaves of water lilies provide some shelter, but the fact that you want to enjoy a clear view of the fish precludes having a large expanse of overlapping leaves. Instead, create an edging of trailing plants to your pond – without a firm foothold, no cat will attempt to reach into the water.

**ALLOW ONE WHOLE DAY**

**Essential tools**

Pointing trowel

Tinsnips

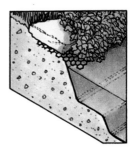

**Making a soft edge**
*Bed a strip of soft wire netting in mortar below flat edging stones. Cut the strip to overhang the water by about 150mm (6in), as a support for trailing plants. Once the plants are established, they will disguise both the wire strip and the exposed edge of a pool liner.*

See also:
Making a small pond, page 102

**Essential tools**

*Mould growth*
Bristle brush
Face mask
Goggles
Large paintbrush
Spatula

*Cleaning*
Face mask
Garden hose
Goggles
Old paintbrush

*Repointing*
Bristle brush
Club hammer
Cold chisel
Face mask
Frenchman
Goggles
Hawk
Pointing trowel

*Spalled brick*
Club hammer
Cold chisel
Electric drill
Masonry bit

See also:
Brightening up a dull wall, page 118
Patching up rendered walls,
page 116

# REFURBISHING AN OLD WALL

Older brickwork has a quality that cannot be matched by new materials. It's not that new brickwork is inferior in any way, nor does it means that current builders are any less skilful than their predecessors. It is simply that over the years weathering tends to create colours and textures that are difficult to reproduce by artificial means.

However, along with these advantages, weathering can cause all manner of problems that need to be tackled in order to preserve old walls. It is unlikely that your particular wall is suffering from every problem listed here – if it is, then you will certainly be faced with more than a weekend's work to fix them. Unless the area of brickwork is very large, you should be able to complete the bulk of any single task in a day, or at most a weekend. Many of these techniques can be adapted for stonework.

# SHIFTING UNSIGHTLY MOULD GROWTH

Colourful lichens growing on garden walls can be very attractive. Indeed, some people actively encourage their growth by painting masonry with liquid manure. However, since the spread of moulds and lichens depend on moist conditions, it is not a good sign when they occur naturally on the walls of your house.

Try to identify the source of the problem before treating the growth. For example, if one side of your house never receives any sun, it will have little chance of drying out. However, you can relieve the problem by cutting back overhanging trees or adjacent shrubs to increase ventilation to the wall.

Make sure the damp-proof course (DPC) is working adequately and is not being bridged by piled earth or debris.

Cracked or corroded rainwater pipes leaking onto walls are a common cause of organic growth. Feel behind the pipe with your fingers, or slip a hand mirror behind it to see if there's a leak.

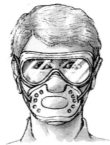

## HEALTH AND SAFETY
Cleaning brickwork or stone can be an unpleasant, dusty job – so wear old clothes, a face mask, goggles and gloves, particularly when working with fungicides and cleaning agents.

## Removing and neutralizing the mould growth
*This is one of those jobs that involves about a day's work in total, but it has to be spread over several days in order to kill off the spores.*

*First remove heavy organic growth, by scraping it from the bricks with a non-metallic spatula. Then, starting at the top of the wall, paint on a solution of 1 part household bleach and 4 parts water to kill the remaining spores.*

*Leave the wall to dry out for a couple of days, then wearing protective clothing (see bottom left), brush the masonry vigorously with a stiff-bristle brush. Don't use a wire brush, as that can damage the masonry. Brush away from you to avoid debris being flicked into your face. Apply a second wash of bleach solution, then leave the wall to dry out.*

## Using a fungicide
If the wall continues to suffer from persistent fungal growth, use a proprietary fungicide (available from most DIY stores).

Dilute the fungicide with water, following the manufacturer's instructions, and apply it liberally with an old paintbrush. Leave it for 24 hours, then rinse the wall with clean water.

In extreme cases, give the wall two washes of fungicide, allowing 24 hours between applications and a further 24 hours before washing it down with water.

# CLEANING DIRTY BRICKWORK

Part of the charm of old masonry is the way it has mellowed, an effect that is due in part to discoloration caused by airborne dirt and pollution. However, if you are bothered by the appearance of your brickwork, you can often spruce it up by washing off surface grime with water. One alternative is to rent high-pressure spraying equipment, which is very efficient for cleaning masonry, but the jet of water is so powerful that it can dislodge loose or cracked mortar and break up spalled masonry. It is therefore safer to use gentler methods on old walls. Even then, avoid soaking brick or stone if a frost is forecast. Strong solvents will harm certain types of stone – so, before applying anything other than water, seek the advice of an experienced local builder who is used to working on the stonework indigenous to your area.

**Washing the wall**
*You can improve the appearance of brick and stone by washing it with clean water. Starting at the top of the wall, play a hose gently onto the masonry while you scrub it with a stiff-bristle brush. Scrub heavy deposits with half a cup of ammonia added to a bucketful of water, then rinse again.*

### Removing stains
Soften tar, grease and oil stains by applying a poultice made from fuller's earth or sawdust soaked in white spirit or paraffin or in a proprietary grease solvent. If you are using a proprietary solvent, follow the manufacturer's instructions.

Wearing protective gloves, dampen the stain with solvent then spread on a layer of poultice 12mm (½in) thick. Tape a sheet of plastic over the poultice, and leave it to dry out and absorb the stain. Scrape off the dry poultice with a wooden or plastic spatula, then scrub the wall with water.

### Stripping spilled paint
To remove a patch of spilled paint from brickwork, use a proprietary paint stripper. Follow the manufacturer's recommendations, and wear old clothes, protective gloves and goggles.

*Stipple the stripper onto the rough texture. Leave it for about 10 minutes, then remove the softened paint with a scraper and gently scrub the residue out of the deeper crevices with a stiff-bristle brush and water. After removing the residue of the paint, rinse the wall with clean water.*

## EFFLORESCENCE

**Removing efflorescence from masonry**
Soluble salts within building materials such as cement, brick and stone gradually migrate to the surface, along with the moisture, as a wall dries out. The result is a white crystalline deposit known as 'efflorescence'.

The same condition can occur on old masonry that is subjected to more than average moisture. Efflorescence itself is not harmful, but the source of the damp causing it must be identified and cured.

*Regularly brush the deposit from the wall with a dry stiff-bristle brush or coarse sacking until the crystals cease to form. Do not attempt to wash off the crystals – they will merely dissolve in the water and soak back into the wall.*

# REPOINTING MASONRY

A combination of frost action and erosion tends to break down the mortar pointing of bricks and stonework. As a result, the mortar eventually falls out, exposing the open joints to wind and rain, which drive dampness through the wall to the inside. Cracked joints may also be caused by using a hard, inflexible mortar.

Replacing defective pointing is a straightforward but time-consuming task. Tackle a small manageable area at a time, using either a ready-mixed mortar or your own mix, consisting of 1 part cement, 1 part lime and 6 parts builder's sand. All the ingredients are available from builders' merchants.

## MIXING MORTAR

Thoroughly mix the dry ingredients on a flat board, then scoop a well in the centre of the mound. Pour some clean water into the hollow, then shovel the dry materials from around the edges into the centre until the water has been absorbed. Blend the ingredients, then once again make a well and add more water until the mortar has the consistency of soft butter.

Mortar containing cement sets in a couple of hours, so don't mix too much at a time. Always wear gloves, goggles and a face mask when handling hydrated lime.

### Preparation

Rake out the old pointing with a thin wooden lath, to a depth of about 12mm (½in). Use a cold chisel and a club hammer to dislodge short sections that are firmly embedded, then brush out the joints with a stiff-bristle brush.

Spray the wall with water so that the bricks or stones will not absorb too much moisture from the fresh mortar.

### TIP ● ● ● ● ● ● ● ● ● ● ● ● ●

### Making a small hawk

You will need a small lightweight hawk for carrying pointing mortar to the wall. Nail a block of wood to the underside of a plywood board, then drill a hole in the block and plug a handle into it.

PICK UP A LITTLE SAUSAGE OF MORTAR ON THE BACK OF A SMALL POINTING TROWEL

### Filling the joints with mortar

Transfer some mortar to your hawk. Pick up a little sausage of mortar on the back of a small pointing trowel and push it firmly into the upright joints. This can be difficult to do without the mortar dropping off, so hold the hawk under each joint to catch it. Try not to smear the face of the bricks with mortar, as it will stain. Use the same method for the horizontal joints. The actual shape of the pointing is not vital at this stage.

Once the mortar is firm enough to retain a thumbprint, it is ready for shaping. Because it is so important that you shape the joints at exactly the right moment, you may have to point the work in stages in order to complete the wall. Shape the joints to match existing brickwork, or choose a profile suitable for the prevailing weather conditions in your area.

## SHAPING THE MORTAR JOINTS

The joints shown here are all commonly used for brickwork. Flush or rubbed joints are best for most stonework. Leave the pointing of dressed-stone ashlar blocks to an expert.

### Flush joint

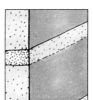

*This is the easiest profile to produce. Scrape the mortar flush, using the edge of your trowel, then stipple the joints with a stiff-bristle brush to expose the sand aggregate.*

### Rubbed (concave) joint

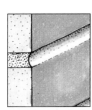

*This is a utilitarian joint that is ideal for an old wall built with bricks that are not of a sufficiently good quality to take a crisp joint. Bricklayers make a rubbed joint using a jointer, a tool shaped like a sled runner with a handle – the semicircular blade is run along the joints. Improvise by bending a length of metal tube or rod (use the curved section only to shape the joint, or you will gouge the mortar). Flush the mortar first, then drag the tool along the joints. Finish the vertical joints, then shape the horizontal ones. Having shaped the joints, stipple them with a brush so that they look like weathered pointing.*

**USING A JOINTER**

### Raked joint

*A raked joint is used in order to emphasize the bonding pattern of a brick wall. It does not shed water, so it is not suitable for an exposed site. Use a piece of wood or metal to rake out the joints to a depth of about 6mm (¼in), and then compress the mortar by smoothing it lightly with a lath or a piece of rounded dowel rod.*

### Weatherstruck joint

*Designed to shed rainwater from the wall, the sloping profile of this joint is ideal for harsh conditions.*

**(SEE RIGHT-HAND COLUMN)**

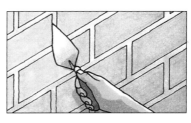

*1* *Use a small pointing trowel to shape the joints. Start with the vertical ones. These can slope to the left or right, but be consistent throughout the same section of brickwork. Then shape the horizontal joints, allowing the mortar to spill out slightly at the base of each joint.*

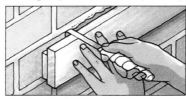

*2* *Finish the joint by cutting off excess mortar with a Frenchman, a tool that looks like a table knife with the tip bent at 90 degrees (see below). You will find it easiest to use a wooden batten to guide the blade of the Frenchman along the joints. Nail scraps of wood at each end of the batten to hold it off the wall. Align the batten with the bottom of the horizontal joints, then draw the tool along it to trim off the mortar.*

### Brushing the face of the wall

Whatever type of joint you choose, let the pointing harden a little before you clean scraps of mortar from the face of the wall. Use a medium-soft banister brush to do this, sweeping it lightly across the joints so as not to damage them.

### TIP ● ● ● ● ● ● ● ● ● ● ● ● ● ● ●

### Making a Frenchman

You can make a Frenchman to finish off weatherstruck joints from a thin metal strip, binding it with insulating tape to form a handle. Alternatively, bend the tip of an old kitchen knife, after heating it in the flame of a blowtorch or cooker burner.

# REPLACING A SPALLED BRICK

In freezing conditions the expansion of water trapped just below the surface of the masonry can cause bricks to spall (flake). If spalling is widespread, the only practical solution is to accept its less-than-perfect appearance, repoint the masonry, and apply a clear water repellent that will help protect the wall from any further damage, while at the same time allowing it to breathe.

More often, spalling affects only a small area of a wall, so individual bricks can be cut out and replaced. Cracked bricks can be replaced in a similar way. However, there is a limit to the number of bricks you can take out without a wall collapsing – so if more than two or three bricks have to be removed, ask a builder for advice before proceeding with the repair.

**Cutting out the spalled brick**
Use a cold chisel and club hammer to rake out the pointing surrounding the brick, then prise out the brick itself. If the brick is difficult to remove, drill numerous holes in it, using a large-diameter masonry bit, then slice up the brick with the cold chisel and hammer; it should crumble, enabling you to remove the pieces easily.

**Inserting the replacement**
*First dampen the opening and spread mortar on the base and one side. Then dampen the replacement brick, butter the top and one end with mortar, and slot the brick into the hole. Shape the pointing to match the surrounding brickwork.*

**TIP** ● ● ● ● ● ● ● ● ● ● ● ● ● ●
**Turning a spalled brick**
If you can't find a replacement brick of a suitable colour, remove the spalled brick carefully, then turn it round to reveal its undamaged face and reinsert it.

# SMARTENING UP A TARMAC DRIVE

You can smarten up an old tarmac path or drive, or any sound but unsightly paved area, by resurfacing with cold-cure tarmac.

It makes a serviceable surface, and is ready to lay straight from the sack.

### Cold-cure tarmac

Cold-cure tarmac is available in 25kg (55lb) sacks that will cover an area of about 0.9sq m (10sq ft) with a thickness of 12mm (½in). You can buy both red and black. Each sack contains a separate bag of decorative stone chippings for embedding in the soft tarmac as an alternative finish. The tarmac can be laid in any weather, but it is much easier to level and roll it flat on a dry, warm day. If you have to work in cold weather, store the materials in a warm place the night before laying. Although it is not essential, edging the tarmac with bricks, concrete kerbs or wooden boards will improve the appearance of the finished surface.

### Removing weeds

*Pull up all weeds and grass growing between cracks in the old paving, then apply a strong weedkiller to the surface two days before laying the tarmac.*

### Filling potholes

Sweep the area clean, and level any potholes. Cut the sides of potholes vertical, remove dust and debris from the hole, then paint the cavity with the bitumen emulsion supplied by the tarmac manufacturer. Wait until the bitumen has turned black before filling the hole with 18mm (¾in) layers of tarmac, compacting each layer until the surface is level.

**ALLOW ONE WHOLE DAY**

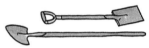

### Essential tools

Garden roller

Rake

Shovel

Spade

Stiff-bristle broom

### TIP ● ● ● ● ● ● ● ● ● ●

**Surface treatment**

If you have an old tarmac path or drive that is in sound condition, you can improve its appearance and extend its life with a protective acrylic coating applied with a brush or paint roller. Such coatings provide an attractive, non-slip surface.

See also:
Laying out a parking space, page 96

## PREPARING THE SURFACE

Apply a tack coat of bitumen emulsion to the entire surface, to make a firm bond between the new tarmac and the old paving. Mask surrounding walls, kerb stones and manhole covers. Stir the emulsion with a stick before pouring it from its container, then spread it thinly with a stiff-bristle broom. Try not to splash; and avoid leaving puddles, especially at the foot of a slope. Leave the tack coat to set for about 20 minutes; in the meantime, wash the broom in hot soapy water. Don't apply the tack coat when there is a possibility of rain.

# APPLYING THE TARMAC

*1 Rake the tarmac to make a layer about 18mm (¾in) thick, using a straightedge to scrape the surface flat. Press down any stubborn lumps with your foot. Spread the contents of no more than three sacks before rolling.*

*2 Keep the roller wet to avoid picking up specks of tarmac. Don't run the roller onto grass or gravel, or you may roll particles into the tarmac. Spread and roll tarmac over the whole area, then compact it by rolling thoroughly in several directions.*

*3 Lightly scatter the chippings before making your final pass with the roller.*

You can walk on the tarmac immediately, but avoid wearing high-heeled shoes. Don't drive on it for a day or two; and if you have to erect a ladder on it, spread the load by placing a board under the ladder. You should always protect tarmac from oil and petrol spillage, but take special care while the surface is fresh.

TIP ● ● ● ● ● ● ● ● ● ● ● ● ● ● ● ● ● ● ●

**Laying a new path**
Although cold-cure tarmac is primarily a resurfacing material, it can be applied to a new hardcore base that has been firmly compacted, levelled and sealed with a slightly more generous coat of bitumen emulsion.

# DRESSING WITH STONE CHIPPINGS

As an alternative to tarmac, completely resurface a path or drive with natural-stone chippings embedded in fresh bitumen emulsion. The emulsion is available in 5, 25 and 200kg (11, 55 and 440lb) drums. A 5kg (11lb) drum will cover about 7sq m (8sq yd), provided that the surface is dense macadam or concrete; an open-textured surface will absorb considerably more emulsion. Chippings in various colours come in 25kg (55lb) sacks, which cover about 2.5sq m (3sq yd).

### Applying emulsion

It takes about 12 hours for bitumen emulsion to become completely waterproof, so check the weather forecast to avoid wet conditions. You can lay emulsion on a damp surface, but not on an icy one. Apply weedkiller and fill potholes, as for laying tarmac.

*Decant the emulsion into a bucket, so it is easier to pour onto the surface. Brush it out, not too thinly, with a stiff broom.*

### Scattering the chippings

*Having brushed out one bucket of emulsion, spread the stone chippings evenly with a shovel. Hold the shovel horizontally just above the surface, and gently shake the chippings off the edge of the blade. Don't pile chippings too thickly, but make sure the emulsion is covered completely.*

*Cover an area of about 5sq m (6sq yd), then roll the chippings to press them down. When the entire area is covered, roll it once more. If traces of bitumen show between the chippings, mask them with a little sharp sand and roll again.*

You can walk or drive on the dressed surface immediately. One week later, gently sweep away the surplus chippings. Patch any bare areas by re-treating them with emulsion and chippings.

### TIP ● ● ● ● ● ● ● ● ● ● ● ● ●
### Double dressing

If the surface you are dressing is in a very poor condition or exceptionally loose, apply a first coat of bitumen emulsion, then cover the surface with chippings and roll thoroughly. Two days later sweep away loose chippings, then apply a second coat of emulsion and finish with chippings.

**Essential tools**

Brick trowel

Rake

Garden roller

Shovel

Spade

Spirit level

See also:
Designing steps, page 94

# MAKING A GRAVEL GARDEN

Low-maintenance gravel drives and pathways feature in many gardens, but you can make more creative use of the colour and texture of gravel – as an attractive contrast to the softer shapes of spreading plants and as a sympathetic background for larger rocks and stones. Areas of gravel for planting are particularly easy to construct and, unless you are planning a large or complex gravel garden, you can complete the work easily in a day.

**Laying out gravel for planting**
*To lay an area of gravel for planting, simply excavate the soil to accept a bed of fine gravel 25mm (1in) deep. You can either set the gravel 18mm (¾in) below the level of the lawn or edge the gravel garden with bricks or flat stones. Scrape away a small area of gravel to allow for planting, then sprinkle the gravel back again to cover the soil right up to the plant.*

# LAYING A GRAVEL PATHWAY OR DRIVE

If an area of gravel is to be used as a pathway or for motor vehicles, first construct retaining edges, consisting of bricks, concrete kerbs or treated wooden boards. This will stop gravel being spread outside its allotted area.

Building pathways takes longer than laying gravel planting areas – because you need to allow extra time for laying and compacting a 50mm (2in) bed of hardcore and for constructing the retaining edges.

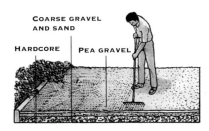

*To lay a gravel drive, the sub-base and the gravel itself must be compacted and levelled, to prevent cars skidding and churning up the material. Lay a 150mm (6in) bed of firmed hardcore topped with 50mm (2in) of very coarse gravel mixed with sand. Roll it flat, then rake an 18 to 25mm (¾in to 1in) layer of fine 'pea' gravel across the sub-base and roll it to make it firm.*

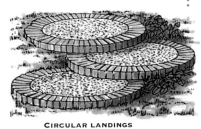

**CIRCULAR LANDINGS**

# INCORPORATING STEPS

Because gravel is so versatile, you have much greater freedom to incorporate curved or flowing shapes into your garden design. Terracing a sloping site with curved gravel-covered steps or landings is as easy as building regular steps from more conventional paving materials. However, building even a short flight of steps will take up most of a weekend.

### Constructing curved steps
To build a series of curved steps, choose materials that will make the job as easy as possible. You can use tapered concrete slabs for the treads, designing the circumference of the steps to suit the proportions of the slabs. Alternatively, use bricks laid flat or on edge. Set the bricks to radiate from the centre of the curve, and fill the slightly tapered joints with mortar.

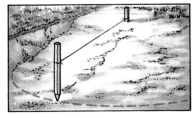

*Use a length of string attached to a peg driven into the ground as an improvised compass to mark out the curve of each step. Terrace the slope by cutting into the soil, and lay concrete-strip or hardcore foundations for the risers. As you construct each step, fill in behind the brick tread with compacted hardcore, allowing for a 25mm (1in) bed of gravel.*

### Building circular landings
*To construct a series of wide landings, build the front edges with bricks, as for curved steps. When the mortar has set, fill the area of the landing with compacted hardcore and lay gravel up to the level of the tread.*

# 4

## THE COMPLETE WEEKEND

ALLOW THE COMPLETE WEEKEND

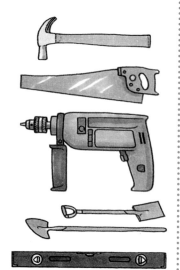

**Essential tools**

Claw hammer

Panel saw

Power drill and bits

Screwdriver

Spade or post-hole auger

Spirit level

Trowel

**Post-hole auger**
*A post-hole auger is a special tool for boring holes in the ground.*

# ERECTING A PANEL FENCE

Fences made from prefabricated panels nailed between timber posts are very common, perhaps because they are particularly easy to erect. Standard panels are 1.8m (6ft) wide and range in height from approximately 600mm (2ft) to 1.8m (6ft); they are supplied in 300m (1ft) gradations. Most panels are made from interwoven or overlapping strips of larch sandwiched between a frame of sawn timber. Overlapping-strip panels are usually designated 'larchlap'; or if the strips have a natural wavy edge, 'rustic larchlap'. You may also see them described as 'waney-edged', referring to where the thin strips of bark were, or maybe still are, attached to the planks.

**Interwoven panel**
*An interwoven-panel fence offers good value for money and makes a reasonably durable screen, but if privacy is important, choose the lapped type – since interwoven strips shrink to some extent in the summer, leaving gaps.*

78

# PUTTING UP FENCE POSTS

Drive a peg into the ground at each end of the fence run and stretch a line between the pegs. If one or more posts have to be inserted across a paved patio, lift enough slabs to dig the necessary holes. You may have to break up a section of concrete beneath the slabs, using a cold chisel and hammer.

### Digging holes

*Bury one quarter of each post to provide a firm foundation. For a fence 1.8m (6ft) high, dig a 600mm (2ft) hole to take a 2.4m (8ft) post. You can hire a post-hole auger to remove the central core of earth. Twist the tool to drive it into the ground, and pull it out after every 150mm (6in) to remove the soil. When you have reached a sufficient depth, taper the sides of the hole slightly, so that you can pack hardcore and concrete around the post.*

### Anchoring the first post

*Ram a layer of hardcore (broken bricks or small stones) into the bottom of the hole to provide drainage and to support the base of the first post. Ask someone to hold the post upright while you brace it with battens nailed to the post and to stakes driven into the ground. (Use guy ropes to support a concrete post.) Check with a spirit level that the post is vertical.*

### Packing with concrete

*Ram more hardcore around the post, leaving a hole about 300mm (1ft) deep for filling with concrete. Mix some concrete to a firm consistency, using 1 part cement, 2 parts sharp sand and 3 parts aggregate. Use a trowel to drop concrete into the hole, all round the post, and tamp it down with the end of a batten.*

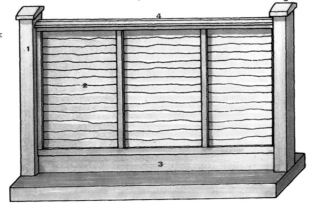

PREFABRICATED PANEL FENCE
1 FENCE POST
2 RUSTIC LARCHLAP PANEL
3 GRAVEL BOARD
4 CAPPING STRIP
5 POST CAP

# FIXING PANELS

Support the first panel on bricks and get someone to hold it upright and push it against the post while you fix it with nails or brackets.

### Skew-nailing

*Skew-nail through the panel's framework into the post. If you can work from both sides, drive three nails from each side of the fence. If the wood used for the frame is likely to split, blunt the nails by tapping their points with a hammer.*

### Erecting the fence

*Construct the entire fence erecting panels and posts alternately. To fill the gaps at ground level, fit pressure-treated gravel boards, using metal angle brackets. Nail capping strips across the panels, if not already fitted by the manufacturer. Finally, cut each post to length and cap it.*

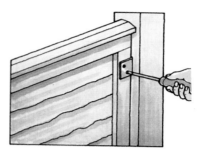

### Using panel-fixing brackets

*As an alternative to nails, use rustproofed metal angle brackets to secure the panels. Drill pilot holes before screwing the brackets to the panels and posts.*

### Topping up with concrete

*Wedge struts made from scrap timber against each post to keep it vertical, then top up the holes with concrete to just above the level of the soil and smooth the concrete to slope away from the post. This will help shed water and prevent rot. If you are unable to work from both sides, you will have to fill each hole as you build the fence. Leave the concrete to harden for about a week before removing the struts.*

ERECTING A PANEL FENCE
1 DIG HOLES FOR POSTS
2 SUPPORT EACH PANEL ON BRICKS
3 HOLD PANEL UPRIGHT
4 NAIL PANEL TO POST
5 FIT GRAVEL BOARDS
6 NAIL ON CAPPING STRIPS
7 CAP POSTS
8 TOP UP HOLES WITH CONCRETE

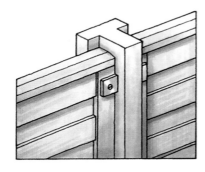

**GROOVED CONCRETE POST**

**RECESSED CONCRETE POST**

**TIP** ● ● ● ● ● ● ● ● ● ● ● ●
**Using concrete posts**
Grooved concrete posts will support panels
without the need for additional fixings.
Recessed concrete posts are supplied with
metal brackets for screw-fixing the panels.

# ERECTING FENCES ON SLOPING GROUND

If you intend to erect panel fencing on
a sloping site, you will need to order
longer posts.

**Crossways slope**
*If a slope runs across your garden so that
a neighbour's garden is higher than yours,
either build brick retaining walls between
the posts or set paving stones in concrete
to hold back the soil.*

**Downhill slope**
*The posts need to be set vertically, even
when you are erecting a fence on a sloping
site. The fence panels should be stepped,
and the triangular gaps beneath them filled
with gravel boards or retaining walls.*

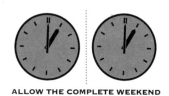

ALLOW THE COMPLETE WEEKEND

### Essential tools

Brick trowel

Builder's line

Hammer

Jointer

Mallet

Mattock

Shovel

Spade

Spirit level

PIERCED CONCRETE-BLOCK SCREEN

See also:
Repointing masonry, page 67

# SCREENING OFF A PATIO

A pierced screen provides a degree of privacy without completely cutting off your view or throwing dense shade onto the patio. It is also relatively easy to build, using cast-concrete screen blocks about 300mm (1ft) square and 100mm (4in) wide. Since screen blocks are not bonded together like brickwork or structural concrete blocks, they require supporting piers. These are made from pilasters 200mm (8in) square, with locating channels to take the pierced blocks. Use coping slabs to finish the top of the screen and piers.

PIERCED CONCRETE BLOCK

**Designing the screen wall**

Building a pierced screen is one of those projects that you cannot complete in a single weekend, mainly because at various stages concrete and mortar have to be left to set hard before you can continue. How much time it takes will also depend on the size and extent of the wall.

Because the blocks are stacked with continuous vertical joints, the piers must be reinforced vertically with 16mm ($\frac{5}{8}$in) steel rods or 50mm (2in) angle iron. If the screen is going to be higher than 600mm (2ft), the blocks will need to be reinforced horizontally too, with galvanized mesh. Position the supporting piers no more than 3m (9ft 9in) apart.

Like all garden walls, a concrete-block screen must be supported on a firm concrete base or footing. If the patio does not already have one, then you will need to allow extra time for laying a footing 400mm (1ft 4in) wide and 500mm (1ft 8in) deep.

# LAYING THE FOOTING

A non-loadbearing garden screen can be built upon a concrete footing laid in a straight-sided trench. The soil must be firm and well-drained, to avoid possible subsidence. It is unwise to set footings in ground that has been filled recently, such as a new building site. Take care also to avoid tree roots and drainpipes. If the trench begins to fill with water as you are digging, seek professional advice before proceeding. If the soil is not firmly packed when you reach the required depth, dig deeper until you reach a firm level, then fill the bottom of the trench with compacted hardcore up to the lowest level of the proposed footing.

**PROFILE BOARD**

### Setting out the footing

For a straight footing, set up two profile boards made from timber 25mm (1in) thick nailed to stakes driven into the ground at each end of the proposed trench but well outside the work area.

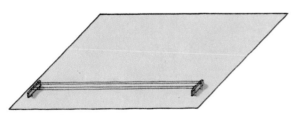

*1 Drive nails into the top edge of each board, and stretch lines between them to mark the front and back edges of the screen. Then drive nails into the boards on each side of the wall line, to indicate the width of the footing, and stretch more lines between them. When you are satisfied that the setting out is accurate, remove the lines marking the screen.*

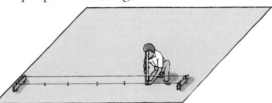

*2 Place a spirit level against the remaining lines to mark the edge of the footing on the ground. Mark the ends of the footing: these need to extend beyond the line of the screen by 600mm (8in). Mark the edge of the trench on the ground with a spade and remove the lines. Leave the profile boards in place.*

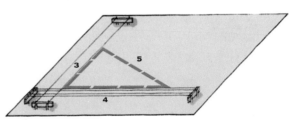

*3 If your screen is to have a right-angled corner, set up two sets of profile boards, as before, checking carefully that the lines form a true right angle, using the 3 : 4 : 5 principle.*

### Digging the trench

Excavate the trench, keeping the sides vertical, and check that the bottom is level, using a long, straight piece of wood and a spirit level.

Drive a stake into the bottom of the trench, near one end, till the top of the stake represents the upper surface of the footing. Drive in more stakes at about 1m (3ft) intervals, checking that the tops are level.

### Inserting reinforcing rods

Drive the reinforcing rods into the bottom of the trench at the required intervals. Check with a spirit level that each rod is upright, then support it with guy ropes until the concrete is poured and set.

### Filling the trench

Mix the concrete (1 part cement : 2.5 parts sharp sand : 3.5 parts aggregate). Pour the concrete into the trench, and tamp it down firmly with a stout piece of timber until it is exactly level with the top of the stakes. Check that the reinforcing rods have not moved, and then leave the footing to harden thoroughly. As this is going to take at least three days, wait until the concrete is surface hard then cover it with polyethylene sheet, weighted down with bricks along the edges, until the following weekend.

# CONSTRUCTING THE SCREEN

To help you mark the position of the screen blocks, restretch the lines between the profile boards. Hold a plumb line or spirit level lightly against each line and mark the concrete with chalk.

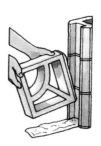

*1 Lower a pilaster block over the first rod, setting it onto a bed of mortar laid around the base of the rod. Check that the block is perfectly vertical and level, and that its locating channel faces the next pier. Pack mortar or concrete into its core, then add two more pilaster blocks on top, packing the core of each with mortar or concrete, so that the pier will correspond to the height of two mortared screen blocks. Check that the pier is plumb and level.*

*Continue with erecting the piers, constructing each in the same way – except that intermediate piers will have a locating channel on each side.*

*Point the piers (concave joints are the most suitable for decorative screening) and allow the mortar to harden overnight.*

*2 Lay a mortar bed for two screen blocks next to the first pier. Butter the vertical edge of a screen block and press it into the pier's locating channel. Tap it into the mortar bed and check that it is level.*

*3 Mortar the next block and place it alongside the first. When buttering screen blocks, take special care to keep the faces clean by making a neat chamfered bed of mortar on each pierced block.*

4 Lay two more blocks against the next pier. Then stretch a builder's line to gauge the top edge of the first course and lay the rest of the blocks towards the centre, making sure the vertical joints are aligned perfectly. Before building any higher, embed a galvanized wire-mesh reinforcing strip, running from pier to pier, in the next mortar bed.

5 Continue to build the piers and blocks up to a maximum height of four courses. Embed another reinforcing strip, then lay coping slabs along the top of the screen and on top of each pier. Finish by pointing the joints.

### Don't build it too high
You can construct a screen up to 2m (6ft 6in) high, but do not build more than four courses of blocks at a time without allowing the mortar to harden overnight.

### TIP ● ● ● ● ● ● ● ● ● ● ● ● ● ● ●
Pale-coloured mortar
If you don't like the appearance of ordinary mortar joints, rake out some of the mortar and repoint with mortar made with silver sand.

# BUILDING A DRY-STONE WALL

Constructing garden walling with natural stone requires a different approach to that needed for bricklaying or building with concrete blocks. A dry-stone wall must be as stable as one built with conventional methods, but its visual appeal relies on the coursing being less regular; indeed, there is no real coursing when a wall is built with undressed stone or rubble.

**Essential tools**

Builder's line

Club hammer

Mallet

Mattock

Spade

Spirit level

Stiff-bristle brush

## DESIGNING THE WALL

A well-built stone wall does not require mortar to hold the stones together, although it is often used to provide additional stability. As a result, many stone walls taper, having a wide base of heavy flat stones and gradually decreasing in width as the wall rises. This traditional form of construction was developed to prevent walls of unmortared stones toppling over when subjected to high winds or the weight of farm animals. Far from being intrusive or detracting from the garden's appearance, this informal construction suits a country-style garden perfectly.

See also:
Laying the footing, page 83

# CONSTRUCTING THE WALL

A true dry-stone wall is built without mortar, relying instead on a selective choice of stones and careful placement to provide stability. Experience is needed for perfect results – but there is no reason why you cannot introduce mortar, particularly within the core of the wall, and still retain the appearance of dry-stone walling.

You can also bed the stones in soil, packing it firmly into the crevices as you lay each course. This enables you to plant alpines or other suitable rockery plants in the wall, even during construction.

When you select the masonry, look out for flat stones in a variety of sizes and make sure you have some large enough to run the full width of the wall, especially at the base of the structure. These 'bonding' stones, placed at regular intervals, are important components, as they tie the loose rubble into a cohesive structure.

Even a low wall will inevitably include some heavy stones. When you lift them, keep your back straight and your feet together, using the strong muscles of your legs to take the strain.

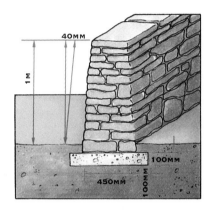

### Building a 'battered' wall

*A dry-stone wall has to be 'battered' – in other words, it must have a wide base and the sides need to slope inwards. For a wall about 1m (3ft 3in) in height – it is risky to build a dry-stone wall any higher – the base should be not less than 450mm (1ft 6in) wide. You should aim to provide a minimum slope of 25mm (1in) for every 600mm (2ft) of height.*

*Traditionally, the base of this type of wall rests on a 100mm (4in) bed of sand laid on compacted soil at the bottom of a shallow trench. For a more reliable foundation, lay a concrete footing 100 to 150mm (4 to 6in) thick. Make the footing approximately 100mm (4in) wider than the wall on each side.*

*1* Assuming you are using soil as a
jointing material, spread a 25mm
(1in) layer over the footing and place
a substantial bonding stone across the
width to form the bed of the first course.

*2* Lay other stones that are about the
same height as the bonding stone
along each side of the wall, pressing
them down into the soil to make a firm
base. It is worth stretching a builder's line
along each side of the wall to help you
make a reasonably straight base. Lay
smaller stones between to fill out the base
of the wall, and then pack more soil into
all the crevices.

*3* Spread another layer of soil on top of
the base and lay a second course of
stones, bridging the joints between
the stones below. Press them down so that
they angle inwards towards the centre of
the wall. Check by eye that the coursing is
about level as you build the wall, and
remember to include bonding stones at
regular intervals.

*4* Introduce plants
into the larger
crevices or,
alternatively, hammer
smaller stones into the
chinks to lock the
larger stones in place.
At the top of the wall,
either fill the core
with soil for plants or
lay large flat coping
stones, firming them
with packed soil.
Finally, brush loose
soil from the faces of
the wall.

**OPPOSITE:**
**TERRACE A SLOPING SITE WITH LOW**
**RETAINING WALLS (SEE PAGE 90)**

ALLOW THE COMPLETE WEEKEND

## Essential tools

Brick trowel

Builder's line

Hammer

Jointer

Mallet

Mattock

Shovel

Spade

Spirit level

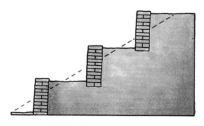

**STEPPED TERRACING WITH RETAINING WALLS**

See also:
Building a dry-stone wall, page 86
Laying the footing, page 83

# TERRACING A STEEP GARDEN

Terracing a sloping site by building a series of low retaining walls is an attractive solution that offers opportunities for imaginative planting. This project may well take a number of weekends to complete, depending on the number and size of the walls, and also because you will need to allow the concrete footings to set hard before you can begin building.

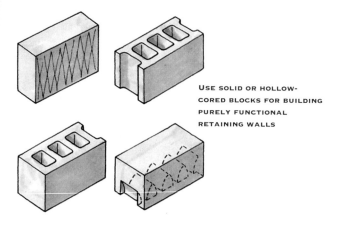

**USE SOLID OR HOLLOW-CORED BLOCKS FOR BUILDING PURELY FUNCTIONAL RETAINING WALLS**

### Choosing your materials

Both bricks and concrete blocks are suitable materials to choose for constructing a retaining wall, so long as it is sturdily built. It is best to support walls of this kind with reinforcing bars buried in the concrete footing. Either run the bars through hollow-core blocks or build a double skin of solid blocks or bricks, rather like a miniature cavity wall, using wall ties to bind each skin together. If you are unfamiliar with standard bricklaying techniques, it may be wisest to get a builder to construct the walls for you.

The mass and weight of natural stone make it ideal for retaining walls. The wall should be 'battered' to an angle of 50mm (2in) to every 300mm (1ft) of height, so that it virtually leans into the bank. For safety, keep the height below 1m (3ft 3in). A skilful builder may be able to construct a dry-stone retaining wall perfectly safely, but it pays to use mortar for additional rigidity.

## TYPES OF RETAINING-WALL CONSTRUCTION

A RETAINING WALL OF HOLLOW CONCRETE BLOCKS

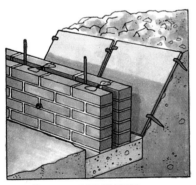

USE TWO SKINS OF BRICK TIED TOGETHER

LEAN A STONE WALL AGAINST THE BANK OF EARTH

# CONSTRUCTING THE WALL

### Laying the footings

*Excavate the soil to provide enough room to dig the footings and construct the walls. If the soil is loosely packed, restrain it temporarily with sheets of scrap plywood or corrugated iron, or similar sheeting. Drive long metal pegs into the bank to hold the sheets in place. Lay the footing at the base of each bank, and allow it to set before you begin building the wall.*

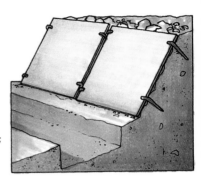

### Laying stones

*Lay uncut stones as if you were building a dry-stone wall, but set each course on mortar. If you use regular stone blocks, select stones of different proportions to add interest to the wall, and stagger the joints. Bed the stones in mortar. It is essential to allow for drainage behind the wall, to prevent*

*the soil becoming waterlogged. When you lay the second course of stones, embed 22mm (¾ in) plastic pipes in the mortar bed, allowing them to slope slightly towards the front of the wall. The pipes should be placed at about 1m (3ft) intervals and pass right through the wall, projecting a little from the face.*

### Finishing stone walls

*When the wall is complete, rake out the joints to give a dry-stone wall appearance. An old paintbrush is a useful tool for smoothing the mortar in deep crevices, to make firm watertight joints. Alternatively, you can point regular stones with flush or rubbed joints.*

*Allow the mortar to set for a day or two before filling behind the wall. Lay hardcore at the base to cover the drainage pipes and pack shingle against the wall as you replace the soil. Finally, provide a generous layer of topsoil, so you can plant up to the wall.*

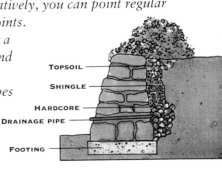

TOPSOIL
SHINGLE
HARDCORE
DRAINAGE PIPE
FOOTING

STONE RETAINING WALL

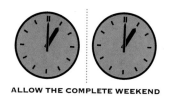

# LAYING A LOG PATH

If a large tree has been felled in your garden, or you live in a rural district where sizable logs are readily available, you can make a practical and charming footpath, using 150mm (6in) lengths of sawn timber, set on end.

Lay the logs together like crazy paving, or use large pieces of wood as stepping stones. To hold wood rot at bay, soak the sawn timber in chemical preserver.

**Essential tools**

Broom

Club hammer

Log saw or chain saw

Mattock

Rake

Shovel

Spade

### Excavating the pathway

*Dig a trench along the line of the pathway to a depth of 200mm (8in). Spread a layer of gravel-and-sand mix 50mm (2in) deep across the bottom – either use ready-mixed concreting ballast or make up the mix yourself. Level the bed by scraping and tamping with a straightedge.*

*1 Place the logs on end on the bed of gravel and sand, arranging them to create a pleasing combination of shapes and sizes.*

*2 Work the logs into the bed until they stand firmly and evenly, then pour some more gravel and sand between them.*

*3 Brush the material across the pathway in all directions until the gaps between the logs are filled flush with the surface. If any logs stand proud, which could cause someone to trip, tap them down with a heavy hammer, until level.*

**TIP** ● ● ● ● ● ●

**Planting between logs**

If you want to plant between the logs, scrape out some of the sand and gravel and replace it with topsoil.

# MAKING STEPS FROM LOGS

If you are able to get sawn lengths of timber from a felled tree, you can use them to build attractive steps that suit an informal or country-style garden. Try to construct risers of a fairly regular height – otherwise someone may stumble, if they are forced to break step. As it is not always possible to obtain uniform logs, you may have to make up the height of the riser with two or more slimmer logs. Alternatively, buy purpose-made pressure-treated logs, machined with a flat surface on two faces. Soak your own timber in chemical preserver overnight.

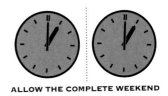

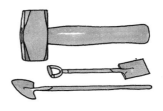

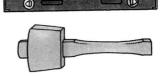

**ALLOW THE COMPLETE WEEKEND**

**Essential tools**

Club hammer

Hatchet

Log saw

Mallet

Shovel

Spade

Spirit level

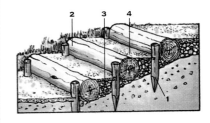

1 Cut a regular slope in the earth bank and compact the soil by treading it down.
Drive stakes, cut from logs 75mm (3in) diameter, into the ground, placing one at each end of a step.

2 Place a heavy log behind the stakes, bedding it down in the soil.

3 Pack hardcore behind the log to make the tread of the step. Shovel a layer of gravel on top of the hardcore to finish the step.

4 If large logs are in short supply, you can build a step from two or three slim logs instead, holding them against the stakes with hardcore as you construct the riser.

**LOG STEPS**
1 RETAINING STAKE
2 LOG RISER
3 HARDCORE INFILL
4 GRAVEL

See also:
Types of preserver, page 35

ALLOW THE COMPLETE WEEKEND

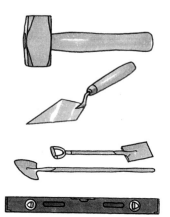

### Essential tools

Club hammer

Pointing trowel

Shovel

Spade

Spirit level

Trowel

# BUILDING A FLIGHT OF STRONG STEPS

Designing a garden for a sloping site offers many possibilities for creating attractive changes of level by making terraced areas or holding plant beds in place with retaining walls. It will probably also involve building at least one short flight of steps, so it is possible to get from one level to another safely.

### DESIGNING STEPS

For steps to be comfortable and safe to use, the ratio between the tread (the part you stand on) and the riser (the vertical part of the step) is crucial.

As a rough guide, construct your steps so that the depth of the tread (measured from front to back) plus twice the height of the riser equals 650mm (2ft 2in). For example, match 300mm (1ft) treads with 175mm (7in) risers; 350mm (1ft 2in) treads with 150mm (6in) risers; and so on. Never make treads less than 300mm (1ft) deep, or risers higher than 175mm (7in).

STEPS BUILT FROM PAVING SLABS
1 CONCRETE FOOTING
2 BRICK-BUILT RISER
3 HARDCORE INFILL
4 PAVING-SLAB TREAD

See also:
Repointing masonry, page 67

# USING PAVING SLABS

Concrete paving slabs in their various forms are ideal for making firm flat treads for garden steps.

Construct the risers from concrete facing blocks or bricks, allowing the treads to overhang by 25 to 50mm (1 to 2in) – so they will cast an attractive shadow line which also defines the edge of the step.

*1 Measure the difference in height from the top of the slope to the bottom to gauge the number of steps required. Mark the position of the risers with pegs and roughly shape the steps in the soil as confirmation.*

*2 Either lay concrete paving slabs, bedded in sand, flush with the ground at the foot of the slope or dig a trench for hardcore and a 100 to 150mm (4 to 6in) concrete base to support the first riser.*

*3 When the concrete has set, construct the riser from two courses of mortared bricks, each course set at right angles to the other. Check the alignment with a spirit level.*

*4 Fill behind the riser with compacted hardcore until it is level, then lay the tread on a bed of mortar. Using a spirit level as a guide, tap down the tread until it slopes very slightly towards its front edge – in order to shed rainwater and so prevent ice forming in cold weather.*

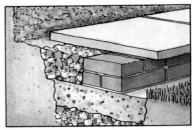

*5 Measure from the front edge of the tread to mark the position of the next riser on the slabs, then construct the next step in the same way. Set the final tread flush with the paved area or lawn at the top of the flight of steps.*

TIP

**Landscaping each side**
It is usually possible to landscape the slope at each side of the flight of steps, and to turf or plant it to prevent the soil washing down onto the steps. Another solution is to retain the soil with large stones, perhaps extending into a rockery on one or both sides.

**ALLOW THE COMPLETE WEEKEND**

**Essential tools**

Bolster/brick guillotine

Broom

Club hammer

Mattock

Plate vibrator

Rake

Shovel

Spade

Trowel

Spirit level

See also:
Types of preserver, page 35

# LAYING OUT A PARKING SPACE

There is no reason why the parking space for a car, or other vehicles, has to be an unattractive expanse of flat concrete. Brick pavers come in a range of subtle colours and shapes, and with care and patience it is easy enough to lay them in an almost infinite variety of patterns.

Ordinary housebricks are often used for paths and small patios, but they are not suitable if the paved area is to be a parking space or driveway, especially if it is to be used by heavy vehicles. For a surface that is more durable, even under severe conditions, use special pavers. These are slightly smaller than standard housebricks, measuring 200 x 100 x 65mm (8 x 4 x 2½in). Red and grey pavers are widely available, and you can obtain other colours by special order.

**Brick pavers**
*Brick pavers are made in a wide variety of colours and textures. Rectangular pavers are the easiest to lay, but other shapes are also available.*

# BRICK PATTERNS

Concrete bricks have one surface face with chamfered edges all round, and spacers moulded into the sides to form accurate joints. Unlike brick walls, which must be bonded in a certain way for stability, brick paving can be laid to any pattern that appeals to you.

**PLAIN CONCRETE-BRICK DRIVE AND PARKING SPACE**

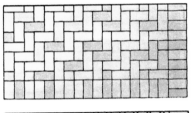

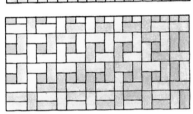

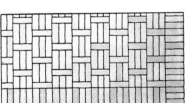

**EXTEND A PARKING AREA TO INCLUDE A LABOUR-SAVING FRONT YARD**

**DEFINE EDGES WITH STONE SETS AND PAVING SLABS**

FROM TOP TO BOTTOM:
HERRINGBONE PATTERN WITH STRAIGHT EDGING
ANGLED HERRINGBONE WITH STRAIGHT EDGING

WHOLE BRICKS SURROUNDING COLOURED SQUARES
STAGGERED BASKET-WEAVE PATTERN
STRETCHER-BONDED BRICKWORK
CANE-WEAVE PATTERN

97

# LAYING A FIRM BASE

Lay down a 150mm (6in) hardcore base covered with a 50mm (2in) layer of sharp sand. Fully compact the hardcore and fill all voids, so that sand from the bedding course is not lost to the sub-base.

Provide a slight cross-fall to shed rainwater and, to protect the building, make sure the surface of the paving is at least 150mm (6in) below a damp-proof course.

## RETAINING EDGES

Unless the brick paving is laid against a wall or some similar structure, the edges of the paving will need to be contained by a permanent restraint.

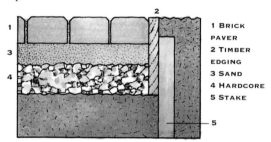

1 BRICK PAVER
2 TIMBER EDGING
3 SAND
4 HARDCORE
5 STAKE

*1 Timber edging boards nailed to 50 x 50mm (2 x 2in) stakes are one solution. The edging boards should be flush with the surface of the paving – but drive the stakes below ground, so they can be covered with soil or turf. Treat all timber with a chemical preserver.*

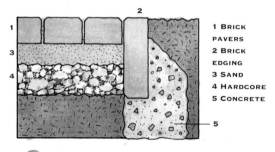

1 BRICK PAVERS
2 BRICK EDGING
3 SAND
4 HARDCORE
5 CONCRETE

*2 A better alternative for a parking space is to set an edging of bricks in concrete. Dig a trench deep and wide enough to accommodate a row of bricks on end plus a 100mm (4in) concrete 'foundation'. Lay the bricks while the concrete is still wet, holding them in place temporarily with a staked*

*board while you pack more concrete behind the edging. When the concrete has set, remove the board and lay hardcore and sand in the excavation.*

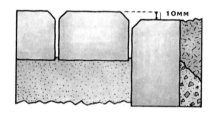

10MM

*3 When bricks are first laid upon the sand they should project 10mm (⅜ in) above the edging restraints, to allow for bedding them in at a later stage.*

*4 To level the sand accurately, lay levelling battens on the hardcore base and scrape the sand to the required depth, using a straightedge. Remove the battens and fill the voids carefully with sand. Keep the sand bed dry at all times. If it rains before you can lay the bricks, either let the sand dry out thoroughly or replace it with dry sand.*

# LAYING THE BRICKS

Having chosen your bricks, prepared the ground and set the retaining edges, you can start laying your paving.

*1 Lay an area of bricks on the sand to your chosen pattern. Work from one end of the site, kneeling on a board placed across the bricks. Never stand on the bed of sand. Lay whole bricks only, leaving any gaps at the edges to be filled with cut bricks after you've laid an area of approximately 1 to 2 sq m (1 to 2½ sq yd). Concrete bricks have fixed spacers, so butt them together tightly.*

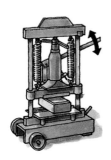

*2 Fill any remaining spaces with bricks cut with a bolster chisel. If you're paving a large area, you can hire a hydraulic guillotine.*

*3 When the area of paving is complete, tamp the bricks into the sand bed, using a hired plate vibrator. Pass the vibrator over the paved area two or three times, until it has worked the bricks down into the sand and flush with the outer edging. Vibrating the bricks will work some sand up between them; complete the job by brushing more sand across the finished paving and vibrating it into the open joints.*

**INTERLOCKING CONCRETE PAVERS**

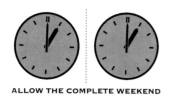

# CONSTRUCTING A ROCKERY

A rockery makes an attractive feature for any garden – and as a bonus, building one gives you an opportunity to use up waste rubble from building projects and soil excavated for a pond. Constructing a rockery can be hard work, especially when moving heavy rocks into place, but the process of creating a unique and thoroughly convincing feature from rock and soil is also a highly enjoyable challenge.

**Essential tools**

Bristle brush

Garden trowel

Shovel

**A convincing rockery**
*Once plants become established, a rockery should blend into a garden without any hint of artificiality. A 'natural' effect relies on the careful positioning of stones during its construction.*

**Small-scale rockeries**
*Don't be put off just because you don't have the room for a large rockery. A successful combination of natural forms can be no less rewarding on a small scale.*

*100*

# BUILDING THE ROCKERY

Select and place each stone in the rockery carefully, to create an illusion of layers of rock. Stones placed haphazardly at odd angles tend to resemble a spoil heap rather than a natural outcrop.

## AN ADEQUATE SUPPLY OF ROCKS

*Buying a sufficient number of natural stones to give the impression of a real rocky outcrop can work out extremely expensive if you order them from a garden centre. A cheaper way is to use hollow-cast reproduction rocks, which will eventually weather in quite well. However, your best option is to purchase natural stone direct from a local quarry.*

*Rocks can be extremely heavy, so get the quarry to deliver them as close to the site as possible, and hire a strong trolley to facilitate moving individual stones about the garden. Take care not to strain yourself when lifting rocks. Keep your feet together and use your leg muscles to do the work, keeping your back as straight as possible. To move a very heavy rock, slip a rope around it and get an assistant to help you lift it.*

*1 Lay large flat rocks to form the front edge of the rockery, placing soil behind and between them to form a flat, level platform. Compact the soil to make sure there are no air pockets, which can damage the roots of the plants.*

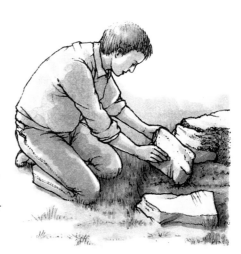

*2 Lay subsequent layers of rock set back from the first, but not in a regular pattern. Place some to create steep embankments, others to form a gradual slope of wide steps. Brush soil off the rocks as the work progresses.*

## TIP
● ● ● ● ● ● ● ● ● ● ● ● ● ● ● ● ● ● ●

**Planting spaces**
Pockets of soil for planting alpines or other small rockery plants will be formed naturally as you lay the stones, but plan larger areas of soil for specimen shrubs or dwarf trees.

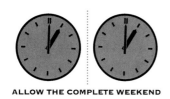

## Essential tools

Bolster chisel

Club hammer

Mallet

Mattock

Paintbrush

Scissors

Shovel

Spade

Spirit level

Tape measure

Trowel

Wheelbarrow

See also:
Building a cascade, page 108
Constructing a rockery, page 100
Protecting your fish from cats,
page 63
Stopping your pond overflowing,
page 17

# Making A Small Pond

There is nothing like still or running water to enliven a garden. Waterfalls and fountains have an almost mesmerizing fascination, and the sound of trickling water has a delightfully soothing effect. Even a small area of still water will support all manner of interesting pond life and plants – with the additional bonus of images of trees, rocks and sky reflected on the placid surface.

### EASY-TO-INSTALL POND LINERS

It is not by chance that the number of garden ponds has increased enormously over recent years – their popularity is largely due to the availability of easily installed rigid and flexible pond liners, which have made it possible to create a complete water garden by putting in just a few days' work. Depending on the size and type of liner, it may take longer than a single weekend to complete the installation, but the bulk of the work can be undertaken in the first two days. You can introduce plants into a pool lined with plastic or rubber as soon as the water itself has matured, which takes no more than a few days.

**Pond under construction**
*This relatively ambitious landscaping project utilizes a flexible liner in the construction of a water garden.*

# CHOOSING A POND LINER

There are a number of options to choose from, depending on the size and shape of the pond you wish to create and how much you propose to spend.

### Rigid liners
*Regular garden-centre visitors will be familiar with the range of preformed plastic pond liners. A rigid liner is in effect a one-piece pond, including planting shelves and, in some cases, recessed troughs for marsh or bog gardens.*

*The best liners are those made from rigid glass-reinforced plastic (fibreglass), which is very strong and resistant to the effects of frost or ice. Almost as good, and more economical, are liners made from vacuum-formed plastic.*

*Provided they are handled with a reasonable degree of care and installed correctly, rigid plastic pond liners are practically leak-proof. A very acceptable water garden can be created with a carefully selected series of pond liners, linked together by watercourses.*

### Flexible liners
*For complete freedom of design, choose a flexible-sheet liner designed to hug the contours of a pond of virtually any shape and size. Flexible plastic liners range from inexpensive polyvinyl acetate (PVC) and polyethylene sheet to better-quality low-density polyethylene and nylon-reinforced PVC. Plastic liners, especially those reinforced with nylon, are guaranteed for many years of normal use – but if you want your pond to last for 50 years or more, choose a thicker membrane made from synthetic butyl rubber. Black and stone-coloured butyl liners are made in a wide range of stock sizes up to 6.5 x 10.75m (22 x 35ft), and larger liners can be supplied to order.*

### Ordering a flexible liner
Use the following simple formula to calculate the size of liner you will need. Disregard the design, planting shelves and so on that you have planned. Simply take the overall length and width of the pond, and add twice the maximum depth to each dimension in order to arrive at the size of the liner. To save money, adapt your design to fall within the nearest stock liner size.

# DESIGNING YOUR POND

A pond must be sited correctly if it is to have any chance of maturing into an attractive clear expanse of water. Never place a pond under deciduous trees – falling leaves will pollute the water as they decay, causing fish to become ill and even die. Laburnum trees are especially poisonous.

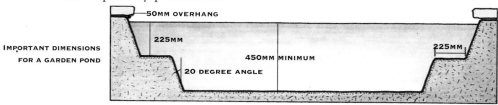

**IMPORTANT DIMENSIONS FOR A GARDEN POND**

50MM OVERHANG
225MM
20 DEGREE ANGLE
450MM MINIMUM
225MM

### The need for sunlight

Although sunlight promotes the growth of algae, which cause ponds to turn a pea-green colour, it is also necessary to encourage the growth of other water plants. An abundance of oxygenating plants will compete with the algae for mineral salts and, aided by the shade cast by floating and marginal plants, will help keep the pond clear.

### Volume of water

The dimensions of the pond are important in creating harmony between plants and fish. It is difficult to maintain the right conditions for clear water in a pond that is less than 3.75sq m (40sq ft) in surface area, but the volume of water is even more vital. A pond up to 9sq m (100sq ft) in area needs to be 450mm (1ft 6in) deep. As the area increases you will have to dig deeper, to about 600mm (2ft) or more, although it's hardly ever necessary to dig deeper than 750mm (2ft 6in).

### Designing the shape of your pond

*Although there is a huge variety of rigid-plastic liners available, you are limited to the shapes selected by the manufacturers. There are no such limitations when using flexible liners, although curved shapes take up the slack better than straight-sided pools.*

*The profile of the pond must be designed to fulfil certain requirements. To grow marginal plants, you will need a shelf 225mm (9in) wide around the edge of the pond, 225mm (9in) below the surface of the water. This will take a standard 150mm (6in) planting crate with ample water above, and you can always raise the crate on pieces of paving or bricks. The sides of the pond should slope at about 20 degrees, to prevent soil collapse during construction and to allow the liner to stretch without promoting too many creases. It will also allow a sheet of ice to float upwards without damaging the liner. Judge the angle by measuring 75mm (3in) inwards for every 225mm (9in) of depth. If the soil is very sandy, increase the angle of slope slightly for extra stability.*

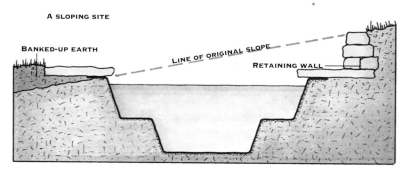

**A SLOPING SITE**

**BANKED-UP EARTH**
LINE OF ORIGINAL SLOPE
**RETAINING WALL**

### Accommodating a sloping site

*On a sloping site build up the low side with earth, turfing up to the paving surround. Cut back the higher side and build a low retaining wall, or bed stones against the earth to create a rockery.*

# INSTALLING A RIGID LINER

Stand a rigid liner in position and prop it up with cardboard boxes, both to check its orientation and to mark its perimeter on the ground.

*1 Use a spirit level to plot key points on the ground and mark them with small pegs. You will need to dig outside this line, so absolute accuracy is not required. As you remove the soil, either take it away in a wheelbarrow or pile it close by, ready to incorporate into a rockery or cascade.*

*2 Lay a straightedge across the top and measure the depth of the excavation, including marginal shelves. Keep the excavation as close as possible to the shape of the liner, but extend it by about 150mm (6in) on all sides.*

*3 Compact the base and cover it with a layer of sharp sand 25mm (1in) deep. Lower the liner and bed it firmly into the sand. Check that it is sitting level, and wedge it temporarily with wooden battens until the back-fill of soil or sand can hold it firmly in place.*

*4 Start to fill the liner with water from a hose. At the same time, pour sifted soil or sand behind the liner. There is no need to hurry, as it will take some time to fill, but keep pace with the rising level of the water. Reach into the excavation and pack soil under the marginal shelves with your hands.*

### Finishing the edges
When the liner is firmly bedded in the soil, either finish the edge with stones or re-lay turf to cover the rim of the liner.

# CONSTRUCTING A POND
# WITH A FLEXIBLE LINER

Mark out the shape of the pond on the ground.
A garden hose is useful for trying out
curvilinear shapes.

*1 Excavate the pond to the level of the planting shelf, then mark and dig out the deeper sections. Remove sharp stones and roots from the bottom and sides of the excavation, in case they puncture the liner.*

*3 When the surround is level, remove the pegs and, to cushion the liner, spread a 12mm (½ in) layer of slightly damp sand over the base and sides of the excavation. Alternatively, cover the excavation with a proprietary pond-liner underlay.*

*2 The top of the pond must be level, and the surrounding stone or concrete slabs needs to be 18mm (¾ in) below the turf. For both reasons, cut back the turf to accommodate the edging stones or slabs and then drive wooden datum pegs, every metre (3 to 4 ft) or so, into the exposed surround. Level the tops of all the pegs, using a straightedge, and check the level across the pond as well. Remove or pack earth around the pegs until the compacted soil is level below their tops.*

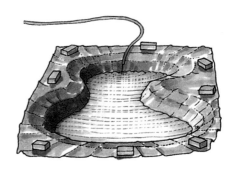

*4 Drape the liner across the excavation with an even overlap all round, and hold it in place with bricks while you introduce water from a hose. It will probably take several hours to fill the pond, but check it regularly, moving the bricks as the liner stretches. A few creases are inevitable around sharp curves, but you will lose most of them by keeping the liner fairly taut and easing it into shape as the water rises.*

# FINISHING THE EDGES OF THE POND

Lay flat stones dry at first, selecting ones that follow the shape of the pond with a reasonably close fit between them. Let the stones project over the water by about 50mm (2in) to cast a deep shadow line and reflection. Wearing goggles, use a bolster chisel to cut stones to fit the gaps behind the larger edging stones.

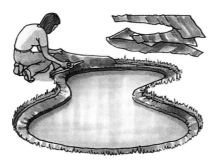

**Cut off surplus liner**
*Turn off the water when the level reaches 50mm (2in) below the edge of the pond. Cut off surplus liner with scissors, leaving a 150mm (6in) overlap all round. Push 100mm (4in) nails through the overlap into the soil, so the liner cannot slip while you place the edging stones.*

**Bedding stones on mortar**
*Lift the stones one or two at a time and bed them on two or three strategically placed mounds of mortar, mixed with 1 part cement to 3 parts soft sand. Tap the stones level with a mallet and fill the joints with a trowel. Use an old paintbrush to smooth the joints flush. Take care not to drop mortar into the water, or you will have to empty and refill the pond before introducing fish or plants.*

**Bringing rocks down into the water**
*Edging a pond with flat stones provides a safe and attractive footpath for tending water plants and fish – but a more natural setting is often required, particularly for a small header pool in a rockery.*

*Incorporate a shelf around the pond – as for marginal plants, but this time to accommodate an edging of rocks. If you place them carefully, there is no need to mortar them. Arrange more rocks behind the edging to cover the liner.*

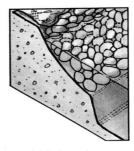

**Creating a pebble beach**
*If you want to create a shallow beach-like edging, slope the soil at a very shallow angle and lay large pebbles or flat rocks upon the liner. You can either merge them with a rockery or let them form a natural water line.*

ALLOW THE COMPLETE WEEKEND

**Essential tools**

Mattock

Scissors

Shovel

Spade

Wheelbarrow

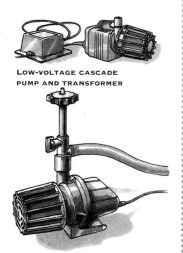

LOW-VOLTAGE CASCADE
PUMP AND TRANSFORMER

COMBINATION FOUNTAIN-
AND-CASCADE PUMP

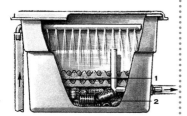

FILTER TANK
1 FOAM FILTER
2 BIOLOGICAL MEDIUM

See also:
Constructing a rockery, page 100
Creating a water feature for your
patio, page 59
Making a small pond, page 102

# BUILDING A CASCADE

A cascade complemented by a rockery planted with alpines or graceful shrubs and trees, such as Japanese maples or dwarf conifers, adds a further dimension to a water garden. The technique for building a series of watercourses is not as complicated as one might expect, and at the same time you can cover much of the groundwork needed for creating the rockery. Providing running water is also an ideal way of filtering your pond.

You will be surprised at the amount of soil produced by excavating a pond. To avoid waste and the chore of transporting it to a local dump, use it to create your poolside rockery. If you include a filter and a small reservoir liner on the higher ground, you can pump water from the main pond through the filter into the reservoir and return it via the trickling cascade.

### Pumps and filters

Small submersible pumps for fountains and cascades are operated either directly from the mains electrical supply or through a transformer that reduces the voltage to 24 volts. Mains electricity and water can be lethal, so get a qualified electrician to help you install the necessary equipment.

Place a submersible cascade pump close to the edge of the pond, so you can reach it to disconnect the hose running to the cascade when you need to service the pump. Stand combined cascade-and-fountain units on a flat stone or securely propped up on bricks, so the jet is vertical.

Pumps usually have built-in foam filters, but these are not sufficient to keep the water in a sizable pond clear and healthy for fish. It is preferable to install a plastic tank containing a combination of foam filters that will remove debris, plus a layer of a biological filter medium to take out pollutants created by rotting vegetation and fish excreta. Conceal the filter tank behind rocks and plants at the back of the rockery, where it can discharge filtered water into the top reservoir.

# TERRACING WITH FLEXIBLE LINER

Rigid-liner manufacturers make moulded cascade kits for embedding into rockeries; you simply cover the edges with stones, soil and trailing plants. Alternatively, create a custom-made watercourse yourself, using offcuts of flexible liner.

### Installing the liner

So that the waterfall can discharge directly into the main pond, form a small inlet at the side of the pond by leaving a large flap of flexible liner (**1**). Build shallow banks at each side of the inlet and line it with stones. Create a stepped watercourse, ascending in stages to the reservoir. Line the watercourse with flexible liner, overlapping the offcuts on the face of each cascade. Tuck the edge of each lower piece of liner under the edge of the piece above and hold the pieces in place with stones. To retain water in small pools along the watercourse, cut each step with a slope towards the rear (**2**) and place stones along the lip to achieve the desired effect (**3**); a flat stone will produce a sheet of water, a layer of pebbles a rippling cascade.

As the construction work progresses, test the watercourse by running water from a garden hose, as it is difficult to adjust the angle of stones once the watercourse has been completed.

Bury the flexible hose from the cascade pump in the rockery, making sure there are no sharp bends, which would restrict the flow of water. Attach the hose to the filter tank at the top of the rockery (**4**).

A rigid-plastic reservoir will have a lip moulded in one edge, which allows water to escape down the watercourse. If you construct a reservoir with flexible liner (**5**), however, you will need to shape the edge to form a low point (**6**) and support a flat stone over the opening to hide the liner.

WATERCOURSE
CONSTRUCTED FROM
FLEXIBLE LINER
1 INLET
2 SLOPED STEP
3 EDGING STONES
4 HOSE RUNS TO
FILTER TANK
5 RESERVOIR
6 RESERVOIR OUTLET

### Terraced watercourse

*This cross section shows a series of cascades running from reservoir to pond.*

ALLOW THE COMPLETE WEEKEND

**Essential tools**

Edging float

Garden roller

Hammer

Hosepipe

Mallet

Rake

Shovel

Spade

Spirit level

Tamper

Wheelbarrow

See also:
Maintaining garden steps, page 32

# LAYING A FIRM BASE FOR A TOOL SHED

Even a small garden shed needs to be erected on a firm, flat base – which will also help to prevent the timber rotting by shedding rainwater. Unless the ground is very uneven or boggy, you can simply lay a pad of concrete paving slabs on a bed of soft sand.

However, a simple rectangular pad of solid concrete makes a more stable and durable base, especially for larger sheds or similar structures. It is not a difficult task, so long as your initial setting out is accurate and you take care with the construction of the necessary formwork. Provided that the base is less than 2m (6ft 6in) square, there is no need to include control joints to prevent the pad cracking.

### LAYING A PAVING-SLAB BASE

Choose simple flat slabs that, when butted together, will make a pad not less than 50 to 75mm (2 to 3in) larger than the shed on all sides. If possible, construct the pad using whole paving slabs, in order to avoid the tedious task of cutting them.

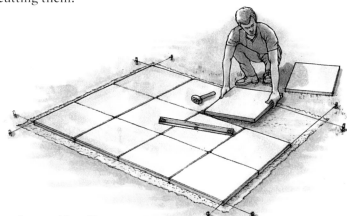

**Laying and levelling**
*Clear and scrape the site level, then spread a layer of soft sand, 25mm (1in) thick, over the area to be paved. Lay the slabs on the sand, butting them together and tamping them down to form a flat, level surface. There's no need to point the slabs, as minor gaps will help to drain away water.*

# LAYING A CONCRETE BASE

### Mixing concrete

For a small shed base, mix 1 part Portland cement, 2 parts sharp sand and 3 parts aggregate (gravel or crushed stone), using a bucket to measure the ingredients. Mix the sand and aggregate on a hard flat surface, then blend in the cement until the colour of the mixture is even. Make a depression for some water, scooping in the dry ingredients until the water has been absorbed; then mix the batch by chopping and turning the concrete with a shovel. Add more water until the concrete is smooth and holds ridges when you drag the shovel across it.

*1 Mark out the area of the pad with string lines attached to pegs driven into the ground outside the work area. Remove them to excavate the site, but replace them afterwards to help position the formwork which will hold the concrete in place. Remove 150mm (6in) of topsoil within the site, to allow for a 75mm (3in) thick sub-base and a 75mm (3in) layer of concrete. Extend the area of excavation about 150mm (6in) outside the space allowed for the pad.*

*2 Cut back any roots you encounter. If there is any turf, put it aside to cover the infill surrounding the completed pad. Level the bottom of the excavation by dragging a board across it, and compact the soil with a garden roller.*

*3 For a straightforward rectangular pad, construct the formwork from softwood planks, 25mm (1 in) thick, set on edge. The planks, which must be as wide as the finished depth of concrete, are held in place temporarily with stout 50 x 50mm (2 x 2in) wooden stakes. Second-hand or sawn timber is quite adequate; if it is slightly thinner than 25mm (1 in), simply use more stakes to brace it. If you have to join planks, butt them end to end, nailing a cleat on the outside.*

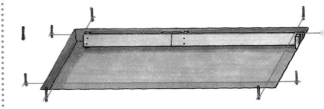

*4 The finished pad should have a slight cross-fall to shed water. Using the string lines as a guide, erect one board at the 'high' end of the pad and drive stakes behind it at about 1m (3ft) intervals, or less, with one for each corner. The tops of the stakes and board must be level and correspond exactly to the proposed surface of the pad. Nail the board to the stakes.*

**5** Set up another board opposite the first one – but before you nail it to the stakes, establish the cross-fall with a spirit level and straightedge. Work out the difference in level from one end of the pad to the other. For example, a pad which is 2m (6ft 6in) long should drop 25mm (1in) over that distance. Tape a shim of timber to one end of the straightedge and, with the shim resting on the 'low' stakes, place the other end on the opposite board. Drive home each low stake until the spirit level reads horizontal, then nail the board flush with the tops of the stakes.

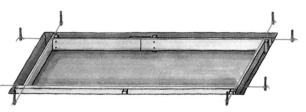

**6** Erect the sides of the formwork, allowing the ends of the boards to overshoot the corners, which will make it easier to dismantle them when the concrete has set. Use the straightedge, this time without the shim, to level the boards across the formwork.

**7** Hoggin – a mixture of gravel and sand – is an ideal material for a sub-base, but you can use crushed stone or brick hardcore provided you remove any plaster, scrap metal or similar rubbish.

Also remove large lumps of masonry, as they will not compact well. Pour hardcore into the formwork and rake it fairly level before tamping it down with a heavy balk of timber. If there are any stubborn lumps, break them up with a heavy hammer.

Fill in low spots with more hardcore or sharp sand, until the sub-base comes up to the underside of the formwork boards.

**8** Mix the concrete as near to the site as practicable, and transport the freshly mixed concrete to the formwork in a wheelbarrow. If the ground is soft, set up firm runways of scaffold boards, especially around the perimeter of the formwork.

Dampen the sub-base and formwork with a fine spray, and let the surface water evaporate before tipping the concrete in place. Start filling from one end of the site and push the concrete firmly into the corners. Rake it level until the concrete stands about 18mm (¾ in) above the level of the boards.

**9** Tamp down the concrete with the edge of a plank, about 50mm (2in) thick, that is long enough to reach across the formwork. Starting at one end of the site, compact the concrete with steady blows of the plank, moving it along by about half its thickness each time.

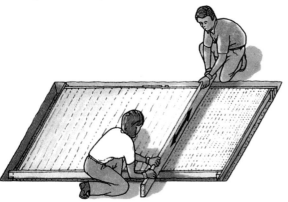

**10** Cover the whole area twice, then remove excess concrete, using the plank with a sawing action. Fill any low spots, then compact and level the concrete once more.

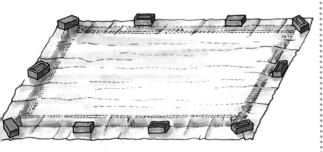

**11** To retain moisture, cover the concrete with a sheet of polyethylene, weighted down with bricks. Alternatively, use wet sacks and keep them moist for three days with a fine spray.

**Insulating concrete**
Try to avoid laying concrete in very cold weather – but if it is unavoidable, spread a layer of earth or sand on top of the sheeting to insulate the concrete from frost.

You can walk on the concrete after three days, but leave it for about a week, to harden further, before removing the formwork and erecting the shed.

**FINISHING THE EDGES**
If any of the edges of the concrete are exposed, the sharp corners could cause a painful injury. Radius the corners with a home-made edging float, as described for rounding over the front edges of concrete steps. Run the float along the formwork as you finish the surface of the concrete.

# A NEW LIFE FOR THE GARAGE FLOOR

Concrete floors are the norm in many modern homes, particularly for utilitarian extensions and garages. In common with a lot of other building materials, concrete can suffer from the effects of damp, as well as cracking and crumbling of the surface. However, repairs are usually relatively easy to accomplish, and resurfacing prior to decorating with a floor paint is quite straightforward. It is the kind of job that takes at least one weekend, to allow sufficient time for materials to set.

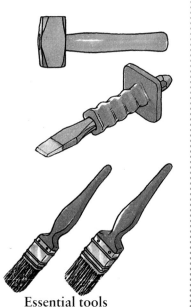

**Essential tools**

Bolster chisel

Club hammer

Cold chisel

Paintbrushes

Paint roller and extension

Plasterer's trowel or float

### Using floor paints

Floor paints are specially formulated to withstand hard wear, making them highly suitable for the concrete floor of a garage or workshop. You can also use them for painting paving stones or steps, and for other concrete structures. Although they come in a limited range of colours, floor paints make an attractive and durable finish for playroom floors, too.

The floor must be clean, dry and free from oil or grease. If the concrete is freshly laid, allow it to mature for at least a month before painting. Prime powdery or porous floors with a proprietary concrete sealer.

**Covering a large floor**
*The best way to paint a large area is to use a paintbrush around the edges, then fit an extension to a paint roller to cover the bulk of the floor.*

114

# FIXING A CONCRETE FLOOR

An uneven or pitted concrete floor must be made flat and level before you apply floor paint. You can do this fairly easily, using a proprietary self-levelling screed, but you must ensure that the surface is free from damp. A new floor should be left to dry out for six months before any impermeable covering is applied, including paint.

### Treating a damp floor

If you suspect that an existing floor is damp, make a simple test by laying a sheet of polyethylene on the concrete and sealing it all round with self-adhesive parcel tape. After one or two days, inspect it for any traces of moisture on the underside.

If this test indicates that widespread treatment is required, paint the floor with a bitumen-based waterproofer, priming the surface first with a slightly diluted coat. Brush on two full-strength coats, allowing each to dry between applications. If need be, you can lay a self-levelling screed over the waterproofer.

An isolated patch of damp suggests that the damp-proof membrane has a small puncture. Use a cold chisel to chop out the damp concrete down to the membrane, and clear away the dust and debris. Paint on two full coats of bitumen-based waterproofer; and when that is dry, seal round the edges of the hole with PVA bonding agent. Fill the hole flush with sand-and-cement mortar mixed with a little diluted bonding agent.

### Patches of oil or grease

Wash a stained garage floor with a proprietary oil-and-grease remover. Soak up fresh oil spillages immediately with dry sand or sawdust, to prevent them becoming permanent stains.

## APPLYING A SELF-LEVELLING COMPOUND

*1 Fill holes and cracks that are deeper than about 3mm (⅛ in) by raking them out and undercutting the edges and then filling them with mortar mix.*

*2 Self-levelling compound is supplied as a powder that you mix either with water or with latex fluid.*

*Make sure the floor is clean and free from damp, then pour some of the compound onto the floor in the corner furthest away from the door. Spread the compound gently with a trowel or float until it is about 3mm (⅛ in) thick, and then leave it to seek its own level. Continue across the floor, joining successive applications of compound until the entire surface is covered.*

*You can walk on the floor after about an hour without damaging it, but leave the compound to harden for a few days before driving a car, or other vehicle, onto it.*

## TIP ● ● ● ● ● ● ● ● ● ● ● ● ●
### Levelling small holes and cracks

For patching small holes and cracks in a concrete floor, a proprietary cement-based exterior filler is a useful alternative to self-levelling compound. After being mixed with water, the filler remains workable for 20 minutes. Just before it sets hard, smooth or scrape the filler level.

**Essential tools**

Banister brush

Bolster chisel

Club hammer

Cold chisel

Foam roller

Mallet

Pointing trowel

Wall brush

Wooden float

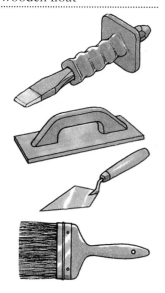

See also:
Brightening up a dull wall, page 118
Refurbishing an old wall, page 64

# PATCHING UP RENDERED WALLS

Brickwork is sometimes clad with a smooth or roughcast cement-based render, both for improved weatherproofing and to provide a decorative finish. Render is susceptible to the effects of damp and frost, which can cause cracking, bulging and staining. Before you redecorate a rendered wall, make good any damage and clean off surface dirt, mould growth and flaky material, in order to achieve a long-lasting finish.

## REPAIRING DEFECTS

Before you repair cracked render, have a builder check the wall for any structural faults that may have contributed to it. Apply a stabilizing solution if the wall is dusty. Ignore fine hairline cracks if you intend to paint the wall with a reinforced masonry paint.

Rake out larger cracks with a cold chisel. Dampen them with water and fill flush with an exterior filler. Fill any major cracks with a render made of 1 part cement, 2 parts lime and 9 parts builder's sand, plus a little PVA bonding agent to help it stick to the wall.

Bulges in render normally indicate that the cladding has parted from the masonry. Tap the wall gently with a wooden mallet to find out the extent of these hollow areas, then hack off the material to sound edges.

*1 Use a bolster chisel to undercut the perimeter of each hole except for the bottom edge – which should be left square, so that is does not collect water.*

*2 Brush out debris, then apply a coat of PVA bonding agent. When it becomes tacky, trowel on a layer of 1:1:6 render, 12mm (½ in) thick, using plasterer's sand. Leave the render to set firm, then scratch it to form a key.*
*Next day, fill flush with a weaker 1:1:9 mix and smooth the surface with a wooden float, using circular strokes.*

# REINFORCING A CRACK

To prevent a crack in render opening up again, reinforce the repair with a glass-fibre membrane embedded in a bitumen base coat. Rake out the crack to remove any loose material, then wet it. Fill just proud of the surface with a mortar mix of 1 part cement to 4 parts builder's sand. When this has stiffened, scrape it flush with the render.

*1 When the mortar has hardened, brush on a generous coat of bitumen base coat, making sure it extends at least 100mm (4in) on both sides of the crack.*
*Embed strips of fibre-glass scrim (sold with the base coat) into the bitumen, using a stippling and brushing action.*

*2 While it is still wet, feather the edges of the bitumen with a foam roller, bedding the scrim into it. After 24 hours the bitumen will be hard, black and shiny.*
*Apply a second coat and feather with the roller. When it has dried, apply two coats of a compatible reinforced masonry paint.*

# A QUICK PATCH FOR PEBBLEDASH

For additional weatherproofing, small stones are stuck to a thin coat of render over a thicker base coat, a process known as 'pebbledashing'. If water gets behind pebbledashing, one or both layers may separate. Hack off any loose render to a sound base, then seal it with stabilizer. If necessary, repair the scratchcoat of render.

*You can simulate the texture of pebble-dash with a thick paste made from PVA bonding agent. Mix 1 part cement-paint powder with 3 parts plasterer's sharp sand. Stir in 1 measure of bonding agent diluted with 3 parts water to form a thick creamy paste. Load a banister brush and scrub the paste onto the bare surface. Apply a second generous coat of paste, stippling it to form a coarse texture. Leave it for about 15 minutes to firm up; then, with a loaded brush, stipple it to match the texture of the pebbles. Let the paste harden fully before painting the repair.*

ALLOW THE COMPLETE WEEKEND

**Essential tools**

Banister brush

Paintbrushes

Paint roller and tray

Paint scraper

**Paint walls in manageable sections**

*You can't hope to paint a large area in one session, so divide the wall into manageable sections to disguise the joins. Here the horizontal moulding divides the wall neatly into two sections, and the raised door and window surrounds form convenient break lines.*

See also:
Patching up rendered walls, page 116
Refurbishing an old wall, page 64

# BRIGHTENING UP A DULL WALL

Although rendered walls were originally intended to simulate the appearance of cut stonework, the dull-grey colour of cement render is unacceptable to the majority of home owners. Consequently, rendered walls are usually decorated with an exterior-grade paint, as are brick walls in some areas of the country. The combination of heat, cold and rain is likely, to some degree, to cause staining, flaking and chalkiness, which need attention before repainting. Decorating an entire house is more than a weekend's work; but depending on the amount of preparation required, you may be able to paint the front or rear wall of a small terraced house in a weekend.

# PAINTS FOR EXTERIOR WALLS

Various grades of paint are produced for decorating and protecting exterior walls, taking into account economy, standard of finish, durability and coverage.

### Cement paint

Cement paint is supplied as a dry powder to which water is added. It is based on white cement, but pigments are added to produce a range of colours. Cement paint is one of the cheaper finishes suitable for exterior use. Spray new or porous surfaces with water before applying two coats.

Shake or roll the container to loosen the powder, then add 2 parts powder to 1 of water in a clean bucket. Stir it to a smooth paste, then add a little more water to achieve a full-bodied creamy consistency. Mix no more than you can use in an hour, or the paint may start to dry.

To provide added protection for an exposed wall and help cover dark colours, add clean sand to the mix to give it body. If you find the sand changes the colour of the paint, add it to the first coat only. Use 1 part sand to 4 parts powder, stirring it in while the paint is still in its paste-like consistency.

### Water-based masonry paint

Most masonry paints are water-based, being in effect exterior-grade emulsion paints with additives that prevent mould growth. Although they are supplied ready for use, it pays to thin the first coat on porous walls with 20 per cent water. Follow up with one or two full-strength coats, depending on the colour of the paint. Water-based masonry paints must be applied during fairly good weather. Damp or humid conditions and low temperatures may prevent the paint drying properly.

### Solvent-based masonry paints

Some masonry paints are thinned with white spirit or with a special solvent – but unlike most oil paints, they are moisture-vapour permeable so that the wall is able to breathe. It is often advisable to thin the first coat with 15 per cent white spirit, but check the manufacturer's recommendations. Solvent-based paints can be applied in practically any weather conditions, so long as it is not actually raining.

### Reinforced masonry paint

Masonry paint that has powdered mica or a similar fine aggregate added to it dries with a textured finish that is extremely weatherproof. Reinforced masonry paints are especially suitable for coastal districts and in industrial areas where dark colours are also an advantage. Although large cracks and holes must be filled before painting, reinforced masonry paint will cover hairline cracks and crazing.

### Textured coating

A thick textured coating can be applied to exterior walls to form a thoroughly weatherproof self-coloured coating. The coating can also be overpainted to match other colours. The usual preparation is necessary, and brickwork should be pointed flush. Large cracks need to be filled, although a textured coating will cover fine cracks. The paste is brushed or rolled onto the wall, then left to harden, forming an even texture. However, if you prefer, you can produce a texture of your choice using a variety of simple tools; this is an easy process, but it pays to put in some practice on a small section first.

Before painting, it is always important to create a sound surface. Below are some common problems you may encounter when decorating previously painted walls.

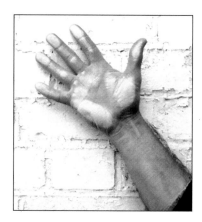

### Chalky surfaces
*Brush the wall with a stiff-bristle brush, then paint the entire wall liberally with a stabilizing primer, which binds the chalky surface so that paint will adhere to it. A white stabilizing primer can also act as an undercoat. If the wall is very dusty, apply a second coat of stabilizer after about 16 hours. Wait a further 16 hours before painting over it.*

### Flaking paintwork
*Flaking is often the result of poor surface preparation or incompatible paint and preparatory treatments. Damp walls also cause flaking – so have them treated, then allow them to dry out before further treatment. Another cause could be too*

*many previous coats of paint. Use a paint scraper and stiff-bristle brush to remove all loose material. Finish the job with coarse glasspaper, or at least feather the edges of any stubborn patches. Stabilize the surface, as for chalky walls, before repainting.*

### Brown staining
*A chimney stack that has the outline of brick courses showing through as brown staining is caused by a breakdown of the internal rendering. This allows tar deposits to migrate through the paintwork. To solve the problem, have a flue liner fitted, then cover the brown stains with a spirit-based aluminium sealer before applying a fresh coat of paint. Treat rust stains caused by faulty metal gutters and pipework with the same primer.*

# TIPS FOR PAINTING THE WALL

A paintbrush is the traditional tool for painting masonry. Choose a brush 100 to 150mm (4 to 6in) wide for painting walls, as larger ones are heavy and tiring to use. On rough walls, a good-quality brush with coarse bristles lasts longest. For good coverage, apply the paint with vertical strokes, crisscrossed with horizontal ones. You will find it necessary to stipple paint into textured surfaces. For faster coverage, use a paint roller with a deep pile for heavy textures and one with a medium pile for shallow textures and smooth surfaces.

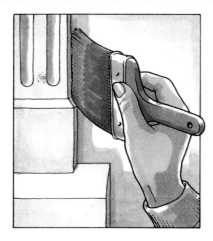

### Cutting in
*Painting up to a feature such as the frame of a door or window is known as 'cutting in'. On a smooth surface you should be able to paint a reasonably straight edge following the line of the feature, but it's difficult to apply the paint to a heavily textured wall with a normal brushstroke.*

*Don't be tempted to apply more paint to overcome the problem – instead, touch the tip of the brush only to the wall, using a gentle scrubbing action, then brush excess paint away once the texture is filled.*

*Wipe splashed paint from the frames of doors and windows with a cloth dampened with the appropriate thinner.*

A BANISTER BRUSH IS IDEAL FOR TACKLING DEEPLY TEXTURED WALL SURFACES

### Painting with a banister brush
Use a banister brush to paint exceptionally deep textures such as pebbledash. Pour some paint into a roller tray and dip the brush in to load it. Scrub the paint onto the wall, using circular strokes to work it well into the uneven surface.

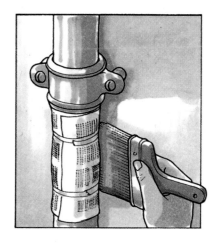

### Painting behind pipes
*Tape a roll of newspaper around rainwater downpipes to protect them from paint. Stipple behind the pipe with a brush, then slide the paper tube down the pipe to mask the next section.*

### Using a roller
Rollers apply paint three times faster than paintbrushes – but they wear out very quickly on rough walls, so have at least one spare sleeve handy. To ensure even coverage, vary the angle of the stroke when using a roller; and use a paintbrush instead to cut into angles and around obstructions.

# GLOSSARY OF TERMS

**Aggregate**
Particles of sand or stone mixed with cement and water to make concrete, or added to paint to make a textured finish.

**Ballast**
Naturally occurring sand-and-gravel mix used as aggregate for making concrete.

**Batten**
A narrow strip of wood.

**Batter**
Slope of the face of a wall that leans backwards or tapers from bottom to top.

**Blown**
To have broken away, as when a layer of cement rendering has parted from a wall.

**Buttercoat**
The top layer of cement-based render.

**Cavity wall**
A wall of two parallel separate masonry skins with an air space or insulation between them.

**Cross-fall**
The angle required to shed water from a flat surface.

**Damp-proof course**
A layer of impervious material which prevents moisture rising from the ground into the walls of a building.

**Damp-proof membrane**
A layer of impervious material which prevents moisture rising through a concrete floor.

**Datum point**
The point from which measurements are taken.

**DPC**
See damp-proof course.

**DPM**
See damp-proof membrane.

**Drip groove**
A groove cut or moulded in the underside of a windowsill to prevent rainwater running back to the wall.

**Efflorescence**
A white powdery deposit caused by soluble salts migrating to the surface of a wall or ceiling.

**End grain**
The surface of wood exposed after cutting across the fibres.

**Feather**
To wear away or smooth an edge until it is undetectable.

**Footing**
A narrow concrete foundation for a wall.

**Galvanized**
Covered with a protective coating of zinc.

**Hardcore**
Broken masonry used to form a sub-base below paving and foundations.

**Heave**
An upward swelling of level ground caused by excess moisture.

**Hoggin**
A fine ballast, usually with a clay content, used to form a sub-base for concrete pads or paving.

**Key**
To abrade or incise a surface to provide a better grip for paint, adhesive or cement-based render.

**Lead**
A stepped section of brickwork or blockwork built at each end of a wall to act as a guide to the height of the intermediate coursing.

**Marine plywood**
Exterior-grade plywood.

**Mastic**
A nonsetting compound used to seal joints.

**Microporous**
See moisture-vapour permeable.

**Mitre**
A joint formed between two pieces of wood by cutting bevels of equal angle at the ends of each piece. *or* To cut the joint.

# GLOSSARY OF TERMS

**Moisture-vapour permeable**
Used to describe a finish which allows moisture to escape from timber or masonry, allowing them to dry out, while protecting them from rainwater or condensation.

**Nogging**
A short horizontal wooden member between studs.

**Pargeting**
The internal render of a chimney.

**Pebbledash**
See render.

**Pilot hole**
A small-diameter hole drilled prior to inserting a woodscrew to act as a guide for its thread.

**Primer**
The first coat of a paint system to protect the workpiece and to reduce absorption of subsequent undercoats and top coats.

**Render**
A thin layer of cement-based mortar applied to exterior walls to provide a protective finish. Sometimes fine stone aggregate is embedded in the mortar, a process known as pebbledashing.

**Riser**
The vertical part of a step.

**Scratchcoat**
The bottom layer (undercoat) of cement-based render.

**Screed**
A thin layer of mortar applied to give a smooth surface to concrete etc.

**Screed batten**
A thin strip of wood fixed to a surface to act as a guide to the thickness of an application of plaster or render.

**Set**
A small rectangular paving block.

**Soakaway**
A pit or trench filled with rubble or gravel into which water is drained.

**Spalling**
Flaking of the outer face of masonry caused by expanding moisture in icy conditions.

**Tamp**
To pack down firmly with repeated blows.

**Thixotropic**
A property of some paints which have a jelly-like consistency until stirred or applied, at which point they become liquefied.

**Tread**
The horizontal part of a step.

**Undercoat**
A layer or layers of paint used to obliterate the colour of a primer and to build a protective body of paint prior to the application of a top coat. See also – scratchcoat.

**Vapour barrier**
A layer of impervious material which prevents the passage of moisture-laden air.

**Vapour check**
See vapour barrier.

**Wall tie**
A strip of metal or bent wire used to bind sections of masonry together.

**Waney edge**
A natural wavy edge on a plank, which might still be covered by tree bark.

**Warp**
To bend or twist as a result of damp or heat.

**Weathered**
Showing signs of exposure to the weather. *or* Sloped so as to shed rainwater.

**Weep hole**
A small hole at the base of a cavity wall to allow absorbed water to drain to the outside.

**Workpiece**
An object in the process of being shaped, produced or otherwise worked upon.

# INDEX

# INDEX

# ACKNOWLEDGMENTS

The authors and producers
would like to thank the following for
their assistance in making this book:

STUDIO PHOTOGRAPHY
Paul Chave
Ben Jennings
Neil Waving
ARTWORK
Robin Harris
INDEX
AND PROOFREADING
Mary Morton

The following companies
and individuals contributed additional photographs
and product information for this book:

DAVID DAY, pages 10, 60.
© JOHN GLOVER (The Garden Picture Library), page 11.
© HARCOSTAR GARDEN PRODUCTS,
Windover Road, Huntingdon, Cambridgeshire, page 23.
© SUNNIVA HARTE (The Garden Picture Library), page 89.
ALBERT JACKSON, page 103.
SIMON JENNINGS, pages 12, 18, 33, 34, 64, 68, 70, 82, 96 top, 97, 102.
© PLYSU BRANDS LTD.,
Wolseley Road, Kempston, Bedfordshire, page 22.
© STAPELEY WATER GARDENS LTD.,
London Road, Stapeley, Nantwich, Cheshire, page 17.
© RON SUTHERLAND (The Garden Picture Library), pages 31 left, 32.
© STEVEN WOOSTER (The Garden Picture Library), page 74.
© Inklink (Ben Jennings Photography),
Jacket & pages 2, 4, 5, 6, 7, 8, 9, 12, 28, 29, 38, 40, 42, 44, 49, 76, 77, 128.

# The Night After Christmas

## JAMES STEVENSON

VICTOR GOLLANCZ LTD · LONDON · 1983

KU-281-568

WARWICKSHIRE
COUNTY LIBRARY
12 JUN 983
CONTROL No.

It was the night after Christmas. Teddy was sitting next to the rubbish bins.

"Jingle bells, Jingle bells," he sang. "Jingle all the way…"

"Why are you singing?" said a doll who was in the bin next door.
"I don't know," said Teddy. "It's better than *not* singing."
"So you got thrown out, too?" said the doll.
"Sure did," said Teddy. "The kid who owned me got a space gun
 for Christmas."

"My name is Annie," said the doll.
"I'm Teddy," said Teddy.
"Merry Christmas, Teddy," said Annie.
"Same to you, Annie," said Teddy.

"The kid I belonged to," said Annie, "got a doll with
hair you can curl and clothes you can change plus a bikini."

"Want to sing 'Jingle Bells'?" said Teddy.
"Not right now," said Annie.

"A word to the wise," said a voice. "They collect the rubbish here first thing in the morning." It was a brown dog.

"Where can we go?" asked Annie.
"You can come to my place," said the dog.
"Thank you," said Teddy.
"Climb aboard," said the dog. "My name's Chauncey."

"It's not fancy," said Chauncey, "but it's warm."

They all went to sleep.

In the morning, Teddy said, "What do we do now?
There's nobody to play with."
"I'll play with you," said Chauncey.
"Thanks," said Teddy, "but I meant children."

"Nothing personal, Chauncey," said Annie.
"That's O.K." said Chauncey. "I'm not much for games anyway.
I run, bark, and wag my tail. That's about it."
Chauncey went out to look for some breakfast.

"You know what we should do?" said Teddy.

"What?" said Annie.

"We should fix ourselves up as new toys," said Teddy. "The kind kids want."

"I am what I am," said Annie. "I can't be anything else."

"Well, I can," said Teddy. "I could be on television.
Kids love that."
"No you couldn't," said Annie.
"You'll see," said Teddy. "Clap if you like it."

Teddy climbed into a box.
"Everybody in the whole family loves Yummy!"
said Teddy. "Tell Mum to buy the large size today!
It's nourishing and delicious!"

"You didn't clap," said Teddy.
"I didn't like it that much," said Annie.
"I have a better idea," said Teddy.
 He went away for a moment.

"What are you supposed to be?" said Annie.
"I am a toy computer," said Teddy.
"Ask me a question."
"How can you be so stupid?" said Annie.
"Is that the question?" said Teddy.

"What now?" said Annie.
"Don't you know a creature from outer space
when you see one?" asked Teddy.

Chauncey came back.

"Having a good time?" he asked.

"No," said Teddy.

"Far from it," said Annie.

"Oh, well," said Chauncey. "You'll get used to it."

For the next few days, Teddy and Annie just sat around,
feeling sadder and sadder.

Teddy began to pace back and forth, back and forth.
"What's the problem?" asked Chauncey.
"I can't get used to getting used to it," said Teddy.

"Hmmm," said Chauncey. He started to leave.
"Where are you going?" said Annie.
"Can we come, too?" said Teddy.
"No," said Chauncey. He was gone a long time.

When Chauncey came back, he wouldn't tell them where he'd been. "You'll find out tomorrow," he said.

The next day he took them down the street.
"Wait till you see," he said.

They stopped at a big building.
"What's so special?" asked Annie.

"You sit there, Annie," said Chauncey, "and you sit there, Teddy."
"I hear a bell ringing," said Annie.

Suddenly, children began pouring out of the doors.

They made a lot of noise, and it took a long time.

When all the children were gone,

Annie and Teddy were gone, too.

Copyright © 1981 by James Stevenson

First published October 1982
Second impression January 1983

*British Library Cataloguing in Publication Data*
Stevenson, James
  The night after Christmas.
  1. Title
  813'.54[J]   PZ7

  ISBN 0-575-03129-8

Printed in Great Britain by W. S. Cowell Ltd, Ipswich